To The Instructor

This Reader, which contains fifteen recent articles from the pages of SCIENTIFIC AMERICAN, is designed as a supplement to the fifth edition of Universe. By having your students read these articles along with the corresponding chapters of Universe, you will be able to provide them with up-to-date information about some of the most exciting developments in astronomy.

Each article is fully integrated with the textbook. For each article, I have written a brief introduction to link the article to what the students have already learned. I have also provided a list of sections from Universe that the students should study before reading the article. Where appropriate, I have also listed relevant animations and videos that you and your students can view on the Universe CD-ROM or at the Universe web site (http://www.whfreeman.com/universe/).

Each article is accompanied by five questions, some qualitative and some quantitative. These are entirely new and have been written expressly for this Reader. Detailed answers to all of these questions can be found in the Instructor's Manual and Resource Guide (IMRG) that accompanies this version of Universe. For more information about the IMRG, contact your W. H. Freeman and Company representative (http://www.whfreeman.com/).

I hope you will enjoy using this Reader as a teaching tool. I certainly look forward to using it with my own students. If you have any questions or comments about this Reader or about Universe, please contact me and I will respond personally.

Roger A. Freedman
College of Creative Studies and Department of Physics
University of California, Santa Barbara
Santa Barbara, CA 93106-9530
e-mail: airboy@physics.ucsb.edu

Be sure to explore the exercises for each article in the back of this Scientific American Reader.

Contents

Introducing "Robots vs. Humans: Who Should Explore Space?" (page 2)

by Francis Slakey and Paul D. Spudis

In the twentieth century, humankind embarked upon the greatest age of exploration in its history: the age of space travel. But in a real sense the space age began in the seventeenth century, when Johannes Kepler and Isaac Newton discovered the basic principles that govern the orbits of the Moon and planets. Today's space explorers—astronauts as well as ground-based scientists and engineers—use the same principles to describe the paths that spacecraft follow as they orbit the earth or travel to Mars, Venus, Jupiter, and beyond.

The first artificial satellite was placed in orbit in 1957, and the first human went into space in 1961. Since then, there has been an ongoing debate about the best way to explore space: with unmanned spacecraft controlled from the Earth's surface, or by humans able to make on-the-spot observations and decisions. The debate on unmanned versus manned spaceflight is particularly relevant today, as work begins in earnest on the International Space Station and as we contemplate the best way to explore Mars.

In "Robots vs. Humans: Who Should Explore Space?" physicist Francis Slakey and planetary scientist Paul D. Spudis present the opposing sides of this debate. Which side of the debate will you agree with? And what do you think should be the character of space exploration in the years to come?

***Before reading this article, study the following:* sections 4-4, 4-6, and 4-7 of UNIVERSE.**

Introducing "Migrating Planets" (page 8)

by Renu Malhotra

We normally think of gravity as an attraction. (A dropped pencil is attracted toward the Earth, which is why it falls down, not up!) But sometimes the gravitational forces between orbiting bodies can actually push them apart. An example is shown in the opening illustration of "Migrating Planets" written by planetary scientist Renu Malhotra. In the illustration, a small orbiting body, or planetesimal, crosses the orbit of Neptune. Although Neptune and the planetesimal do not actually collide, they undergo scattering: the gravitational forces that the two objects exert on each other alter their trajectories. As a result, Neptune and the planetesimal move away from each other, Neptune into a slightly larger orbit, the planetesimal into a smaller one. A second scattering between the planetesimal and Jupiter pushes these two objects apart: Jupiter goes into a slightly smaller orbit, while the planetesimal goes into a much larger one that takes it completely out of the solar system.

Scattering of planetesimals is thought to have been common in the first several million years after the formation of the planets. As the article describes, these events may have dramatically altered the orbits of the outermost planets and helped create a swarm of small, icy objects that orbit beyond Neptune. The theory described here may rewrite the story of how the planets formed and may help us understand the character of planets that orbit other stars.

***Before reading this article, study the following:* sections 7-7, 7-8, and 7-9 of UNIVERSE; the essay "Alien Planets" by Geoff Marcy on pages 189–190 of UNIVERSE.**

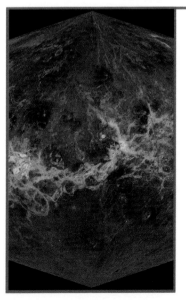

Introducing "Global Climate Change on Venus" (page 16)

by Mark A. Bullock and David H. Grinspoon

It is hard to imagine a less inviting place to visit than the surface of Venus. Temperatures there are hundreds of degrees higher than the inside of a kitchen oven. The pressure of the carbon dioxide atmosphere is great enough to crush the hull of a submarine. As described in Section 11-3 of Universe, this thick atmosphere is what keeps the temperature so high. Carbon dioxide efficiently traps infrared light coming from the planet's surface, making it difficult for the planet to radiate its heat into space.

Yet as hellish a place as Venus is today, it may have been even more so several hundred million years ago. As planetary scientists Mark A. Bullock and David H. Grinspoon describe in the following article, volcanic activity across the face of the planet flooded the surface with lava and belched massive quantities of water vapor and sulfur dioxide into the air. These gases caused Venus's surface temperature to vary up and down by hundreds of degrees. Remarkably, these temperature variations may have helped to actually reshape the surface of the planet. Studying the dramatic effects of such global climate changes on Venus may help us better understand the changes that we humans are causing in our own atmosphere.

***Before reading this article, study the following:* sections 8-6, 11-3, 11-4, 11-5, 11-6, and 11-7 of UNIVERSE; the following animations and videos from Chapter 11 of the Universe CD-ROM or web site: "Magellan Maps a Planet," "Volcanoes on Venus," "Craters, Volcanoes, and Highlands on Venus," "An Immense Chasm on Venus," and "Impact Craters and Volcanoes on Venus"; the module "Venus" from the "Planetary Geology" section of the Universe CD-ROM or web site.**

Contents

One of the most dramatic aspects of the past forty years of space exploration has been the exploration of Mars. As described in Section 12-3 of Universe, each new spacecraft that has flown past, orbited, or landed on Mars has transformed our understanding of the red planet.

As in all great dramas, the story of Martian exploration has included its share of tragedy. The most recent (1999) was the loss of the Mars Climate Orbiter and Mars Polar Lander spacecraft, neither of which arrived successfully at Mars. In all, 11 of the 25 spacecraft launched toward Mars since 1962 have failed to reach their goal. These statistics remind us what a challenging task it is to design, build, and launch a complicated spacecraft, have it travel hundreds of millions of kilometers through space, and arrive at a precise location on a hostile alien planet. Appreciating the magnitude of this challenge makes the successful missions to Mars seem even more remarkable.

One of the most successful of all Martian missions was Mars Pathfinder, which in 1997 became the first to place a wheeled vehicle on the planet's surface. This mission and its findings are described briefly in Section 12-10 of Universe. This article by Matthew P. Golombek, the project scientist for Mars Pathfinder, provides an in-depth look at the spacecraft, the work it carried out on the Martian surface, and the remarkable discoveries it made about the geologic history of Mars.

Before reading this article, study the following: sections 12-3, 12-4, 12-5, 12-6, 12-7, 12-8, and 12-10 of UNIVERSE; the following videos from Chapter 12 of the Universe CD-ROM or web site: "Valles Marineris and the Giant Volcanoes of Mars," "A Martian Chasm," and "Surface of Mars as Seen by the Viking 1 Lander"; the module "Mars" from the "Planetary Geology" section of the Universe CD-ROM or web site.

One of the most unique and surprising worlds in the solar system is Europa, the smallest of the four Galilean satellites of Jupiter. A world of this small size should be geologically inactive, with a cratered surface like that of the Moon. But as Section 14-6 of Universe describes, Europa's icy surface is crisscrossed with a bewildering assortment of cracks, streaks, bands, and jumbled terrain. These features are stark evidence of a very active geological history, and suggest that Europa is geologically active today. They also indicate that beneath the rigid surface ice lies a layer of either liquid water or warm, soft ice. In other words, water and ice may play the same roles in Europa's geology that lava and solid rock do in Earth's.

Most of what we know about Europa has been learned in the last few years, thanks to the Galileo spacecraft in orbit around Jupiter. Among the many discoveries made by Galileo are the nature and extent of Europa's surface features, clues to the chemistry of Europa's interior, and tantalizing suggestions of plate tectonic activity. In "The Hidden Ocean of Europa" Robert T. Pappalardo, James W. Head, and Ronald Greeley—planetary scientists, Europa specialists, and Galileo team members — provide a detailed look at these discoveries. They also describe plans for even more ambitious missions to explore this icy yet dynamic world.

Before reading this article, study the following: sections 14-1, 14-4, and 14-6 of UNIVERSE; the following videos from Chapter 14 of the Universe CD-ROM or web site: "Jupiter's Moon Io" and "A Simulated Flight Over Io."

A comet bright enough to be visible to the naked eye is a rather rare and memorable celestial event. (Seeing two bright comets in as many years—such as happened with Comet Hyakutake in 1996 and Comet Hale-Bopp in 1997—is very exceptional.) But imagine that such comets were hundreds of times more numerous and that some of them actually struck the Earth's surface. What effect would this have on our planet and our atmosphere? And could living creatures, including humans, survive such a cataclysm?

Such ideas are not just science fiction. In "The Oort Cloud" comet researcher Paul R. Weissman explains how just such a comet "shower" could take place, and gives evidence that such an event has actually occurred in the Earth's past. The key to understanding such cosmic cataclysms, as well as more ordinary sorts of comets, lies in an appreciation of the region of space from which many comets come. This region, which extends far beyond the orbit of Pluto to the outermost fringes of the solar system, is called the Oort cloud. Though remote and seemingly unconnected to our daily lives, the Oort cloud and the comets it contains may have played a role in the history of life on Earth. It may also contain clues to the very beginnings of our solar system.

Before reading this article, study the following: sections 17-7, 17-8, and 17-9 of UNIVERSE; the essay "Discovering a Comet" by Alan Hale on pages 416–417 of UNIVERSE.

Contents

Introducing "SOHO Reveals the Secrets of the Sun" (page 48)

by Kenneth R. Lang

The largest, most massive, and by far most dynamic object in the solar system is the Sun itself. As you have read in Chapter 18 of Universe, the solar surface oscillates in and out in a complex way, streams of hot gas flow perpetually outward from the solar atmosphere, and from time to time massive clumps of matter are ejected from above the equatorial regions of the Sun. This solar activity can have a direct effect on us here on Earth. When the Sun is at its most active—as in 2000—tremendous amounts of material from the Sun can reach the Earth. This can cause beautiful and impressive auroral displays but also has the potential to wreak havoc on radio transmissions, damage electrical equipment, and pose a radiation hazard to unprotected astronauts.

Observatories to study the Sun are found at various locations around the Earth. One of the most powerful and capable solar observatories, however, is located more than a million kilometers from Earth. This is the spacecraft SOHO (Solar and Heliospheric Observatory), which has been observing the Sun since 1995. With its diverse suite of instruments, SOHO has helped us learn not only about the visible surface of the Sun but also about its thin, high-temperature outer atmosphere and its deep interior. This article, by solar astronomer Kenneth R. Lang, describes some of these remarkable discoveries.

Before reading this article, study the following: **sections 18-1, 18-2, 18-3, 18-4, 18-5, 18-6, 18-7, and 18-8 of UNIVERSE; the following animations and videos from Chapter 18 of the Universe CD-ROM or web site: "Granules on the Sun's Surface," "Convection in the Photosphere," "An X-Ray Look at the Sun," "Seething Granules Around Sunspots," "The Motion of a Small Sunspot Group," and "Seismic Quakes on the Sun."**

Introducing "Detecting Massive Neutrinos" (page 54)

by Edward Kearns, Takaaki Kajita and Yoji Totsuka

For the past thirty years, one of the great unanswered questions about the Sun has been: "Where are the neutrinos?" As described in Section 18-6 of Universe, neutrinos are subatomic particles that are created as a by-product of nuclear fusion reactions within the Sun. The number of neutrinos that reach us on Earth should therefore tell us how rapidly these reactions are taking place. But all solar neutrino experiments to date have detected substantially fewer neutrinos than expected. Does this mean that nuclear reactions are happening at a slower rate than we had thought? If so, something may be terribly wrong with our models of the Sun's internal structure. Or could it be that the neutrinos themselves are not behaving as expected?

Circumstantial evidence in favor of the second explanation began to appear in 1998. Data from the Super Kamiokande (Super-K, for short) neutrino detector in Japan strongly suggested that neutrinos of one type were actually transforming into neutrinos of a second type—in other words, these particles were changing their identity. Neutrinos can only do this thanks to the curious properties of quantum mechanics, the branch of physics that explains the nature of matter and energy on the smallest scales. How this discovery was made, and what it may imply for our understanding of the Sun, is the subject of this article by neutrino physicists Edward Kearns, Takaaki Kajita, and Yoji Totsuka.

Before reading this article, study the following: **sections 18-6 and 18-9 of UNIVERSE; the essay "Searching for Neutrinos Beyond the Textbooks" by John N. Bahcall on pages 452–453 of UNIVERSE.**

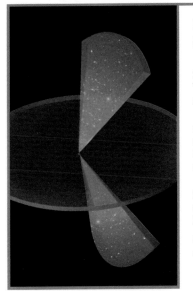

Introducing "Mapping the Universe" (page 62)

by Stephen D. Landy

On a dark, moonless night far from city lights, you can see several thousand stars with the unaided eye. At first glance, the stars seem to be strewn randomly across the sky. But soon you will notice the band of the Milky Way, a glowing arc of starlight that stretches across the sky. This band is evidence that the stars are not in truly random locations, but are clumped into the disk of our Galaxy (see Figure 25-1 on page 615 of Universe).

Over the past several decades, astronomers have discovered that the universe is clumped on several different scales. Galaxies like our own are clumped into clusters millions of light-years across, and clusters are themselves clumped into superclusters that can extend for hundreds of millions of light-years. But superclusters are not the largest structures of the universe. In recent years new techniques have been used to identify immense bands, or walls, of galaxies. The dimensions of these walls dwarf even the largest supercluster.

How have astronomers made these discoveries? What has made the matter of our universe clump in these different ways? And what does this tell us about the early history of the universe? In "Mapping the Universe" astronomer Stephen D. Landy explains the answers to these questions and describes how he and his collaborators have been able to analyze the universe using techniques borrowed from the study of music and noise.

Before reading this article, study the following: **sections 26-4, 26-5, 26-6, and 26-8 of UNIVERSE; the essay "The Great Attractor" by Alan Dressler on pages 669–670 of UNIVERSE.**

Contents

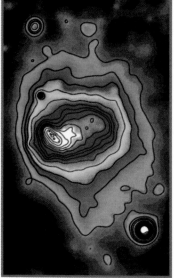

Introducing "The Evolution of Galaxy Clusters" (page 70)

by J. Patrick Henry, Ulrich G. Briel and Hans Böhringer

To the casual observer of the night sky, the stars appear permanent and unchanging. But as you have learned from your study of Universe, the stars are anything but static. New stars are constantly being formed within dark nebulae. Within their cores, these stars are converting hydrogen into helium at a prodigious rate. And when these stars die, they eject much of their matter back into interstellar space—matter that is enriched in heavy elements and that will someday go into making a new population of stars. The seeming constancy of starlight is merely an illusion.

Far beyond our own Galaxy lie objects that likewise appear at first glance to be static. These are galaxy clusters, immense associations of galaxies that stay together thanks to their mutual gravitational attraction. But just as studies of the stars have revealed how they evolve, observations of galaxy clusters have shown that they, too, lead dynamic and ever-changing lives. As you will learn in "The Evolution of Galaxy Clusters" by astronomers J. Patrick Henry, Ulrich G. Briel, and Hans Böhringer, clusters of galaxies grow by absorbing other, smaller galaxy groupings. As the number of galaxies in a cluster increases, so does the size of the gas cloud that surrounds them—a cloud that dwarfs the galaxies in size and in mass and that is so hot that it emits X rays. Most remarkable of all, the evolution of these behemoth clusters of galaxies and gas may tell us about the eventual fate of our universe.

Before reading this article, study the following: sections 26-6, 26-7, and 26-8 of UNIVERSE.

Introducing "A New Look At Quasars" (page 76)

by Michael Disney

For the past four decades, quasars have been among the greatest puzzles in astronomy. What is the nature of these incredibly remote, incredibly luminous objects? How can something so small on the cosmic scale—perhaps a mere dozen times larger than our solar system—be hundreds of times more luminous than an entire galaxy? What is the connection between quasars and galaxies? How do quasars form, and how do they evolve? And why did quasars exist in copious numbers a few billion years after the Big Bang, but are all but absent from our present-day universe?

These questions and others have challenged generations of astronomers. In this article, quasar specialist Michael Disney tells the story of the innovative approaches that he and his colleagues have taken to the study of quasars, and describes the tremendous progress that has been made in understanding these objects. He also tells the story of the frustration felt by quasar astronomers using the Hubble Space Telescope, which has hindered as well as helped their research—and how planned upgrades to the telescope may help it fulfill its promise for unlocking the secrets of quasars. (Note: The Advanced Camera for Surveys, described in Disney's article, is scheduled to be installed in 2001.)

Before reading this article, study the following: sections 27-1, 27-2, 27-3, 27-4, 27-5, and 27-6 of UNIVERSE; the following animations from Chapter 27 of the Universe CD-ROM or web site: "The Central Engine of an Active Galaxy," "A Supermassive Black Hole in an Active Galaxy," and "Zooming into an Active Galaxy."

Introducing "Gamma-Ray Bursts" (page 82)

by Gerald J. Fishman and Dieter H. Hartmann

Like quasars, gamma-ray bursts (or "bursters") have perplexed astronomers for many years. There has been great confusion over whether these sources of intense, short-lived gamma rays lie within our Milky Way Galaxy or far beyond it. A major complication is that gamma-ray telescopes have had poor angular resolution, making it difficult to pinpoint the exact location of a burst. Another is that the bursts are short-lived, typically lasting no more than a few seconds.

As you have read in Box 27-2 of Universe, the study of gamma-ray bursts underwent a revolution in 1997. In this article, Gerald J. Fishman and Dieter H. Hartmann—an experimenter and a theoretical astrophysicist, respectively, both of whom have been deeply involved in the study of gamma-ray bursts—explain how this revolution came about. They also describe some of the theoretical models that have been proposed to explain how gamma-ray bursts happen. Whatever gamma-ray bursts turn out to be, it is clear that along with supernovae, they involve the greatest explosions that our universe has seen since the Big Bang.

For even more recent information on the rapidly evolving subject of gamma-ray bursts, visit the NASA web site http://www.batse.com/.

Before reading this article, study the following: boxes 27-2 and 27-3 on pages 676 and 677 of UNIVERSE.

Contents

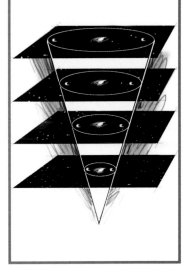

Introducing "Surveying Space-time with Supernovae" (page 88)

by Craig J. Hogan, Robert P. Kirshner and Nicholas B. Suntzeff

When fireworks explode in midair, glowing debris flies in every direction. As it moves, the debris slows down because of the retarding effects of air resistance. Even if fireworks could explode in space, far above the atmosphere, the debris would still slow down because of its mutual gravitational attraction. Imagine, then, how surprised you would be if the debris actually sped up as it flew away from the explosion! Such accelerated motion would seem to defy the laws of physics.

Amazingly, the expansion of our entire universe may be speeding up in just this way. This remarkable, unexpected, and controversial result is one of the biggest news stories to come out of science in the past several years.

In "Surveying Space-time with Supernovae" astronomers Craig J. Hogan, Robert P. Kirshner, and Nicholas B. Suntzeff describe how they and their colleagues have been able to trace the history of the expansion of the universe. The key to their approach is to watch distant galaxies for Type Ia supernovae, immense stellar explosions whose light can be seen even across billions of light-years. Observations of such supernovae make it possible to determine the distance to the supernova and the galaxy to which it belongs, as well as the recessional velocity of the host galaxy. What follows is a scientific detective story whose solution may change our understanding of the history and the very nature of our universe.

Before reading this article, study the following: sections 22-9, 26-4, 28-1, 28-2, 28-3, 28-6, 28-7, and 28-8 of UNIVERSE.

Introducing "Cosmological Antigravity" (page 94)

by Lawrence M. Krauss

"How empty is space?" This seemingly foolish question is, in fact, one of the greatest conundrums in cosmology. In terminology more appropriate for astronomy, the question is "What is the average density of matter in the universe?" Until very recently, and for a variety of compelling theoretical and observational reasons, many astronomers felt that the average density of matter was equal to the critical density, a special value that just barely allows the universe to expand forever without collapsing back on itself. But the most recent surveys of the amount of matter in the universe, even those that include the elusive dark matter, have found that the average density of matter is no more than half of the critical density. In other words, "empty" space is even emptier than had been imagined.

But the total average density may indeed be close to the critical density, if we include the effects of a curious sort of energy that fills all of space. Einstein first proposed this energy in terms of the cosmological constant, a term added to his equations for the general theory of relativity. Unlike ordinary matter, which attracts other matter by gravity and slows the expansion of the universe, this energy helps the universe to expand as though it possessed "antigravity." (To learn more about some of the evidence for this model, see the article "Surveying Space-time with Supernovae" by Craig J. Hogan, Robert P. Kirshner, and Nicholas B. Suntzeff, included in this Reader.) In "Cosmological Antigravity" astrophysicist Lawrence M. Krauss describes how he and other researchers have been led to these remarkable and controversial ideas.

Before reading this article, study the following: sections 28-1, 28-2, 28-3, 28-6, 28-7, and 28-8 and Box 28-3 of UNIVERSE.

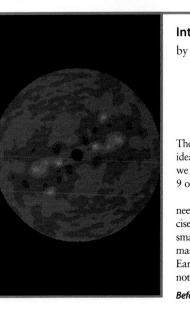

Introducing "Searching for Life in Other Solar Systems" (page 102)

by Roger Angel and Neville J. Woolf

> There are countless suns and countless earths all rotating around
> their suns. ...We see only the suns because they are the largest bodies
> and most luminous, but their planets remain invisible to us because they
> are smaller and non-luminous. The countless worlds of the universe are
> no worse and no less inhabited than our Earth.

The Italian cleric and philosopher Giordano Bruno penned these visionary words in 1584. At the time, Bruno's ideas were considered extremely radical and dangerous and led to his being burned at the stake in 1600. Today, we know that Bruno was at least partly correct, because we now have concrete evidence (described in Section 7-9 of Universe) that there are indeed planets orbiting other stars.

But are any of these worlds "no worse and no less inhabited than our Earth"? To answer this question, we need a way to identify terrestrial planets orbiting other stars. This is an extremely challenging task, and for precisely the reason that Bruno gave four centuries ago: A planet like the Earth orbiting another star would be too small and too dim to be seen against the glare of the star's light. In "Searching for Life in Other Solar Systems" master telescope makers Roger Angel and Neville J. Woolf describe how a special space telescope could detect Earthlike planets beyond the solar system—and how such a telescope may actually come into existence in the not too distant future.

Before reading this article, study the following: sections 7-9, 30-1, 30-2, 30-3, and 30-4 of UNIVERSE.

ROBOTS v

Who Should

Unmanned spacecraft are exploring the solar system more cheaply and effectively than astronauts are

by Francis Slakey

The National Aeronautics and Space Administration has a difficult task. It must convince U.S. taxpayers that space science is worth $13.6 billion a year. To achieve this goal, the agency conducts an extensive public-relations effort that is similar to the marketing campaigns of America's biggest corporations. NASA has learned a valuable lesson about marketing in the 1990s: to promote its programs, it must provide entertaining visuals and stories with compelling human characters. For this reason, NASA issues a steady stream of press releases and images from its human spaceflight program.

Every launch of the space shuttle is a media event. NASA presents its astronauts as ready-made heroes, even when their accomplishments in space are no longer groundbreaking. Perhaps the best example of NASA's public-relations prowess was the participation of John Glenn, the first American to orbit Earth, in shuttle mission STS-95 last year. Glenn's return to space at the age of 77 made STS-95 the most avidly followed mission since the Apollo moon landings. NASA claimed that Glenn went up for science—he served as a guinea pig in various medical experiments—but it was clear that the main benefit of Glenn's space shuttle ride was publicity, not scientific discovery.

Continued on page 4

NASA AND CARNEGIE MELLON UNIVERSITY

NOMAD ROVER developed by the Robotics Institute at Carnegie Mellon University is shown traversing the icy terrain of Antarctica late last year. Scientists are testing the prototype in inhospitable environments on Earth to develop an advanced rover for future unmanned space missions.

s. HUMANS

Explore Space?

Astronaut explorers can perform science in space that robots cannot

by Paul D. Spudis

APOLLO 17 ASTRONAUT Harrison Schmitt investigates a huge boulder at the Taurus-Littrow landing site on the moon in 1972. Schmitt, a geologist, made important discoveries about the moon's composition and history, thus demonstrating the value of astronauts as space explorers.

Criticism of human spaceflight comes from many quarters. Some critics point to the high cost of manned missions. They contend that the National Aeronautics and Space Administration has a full slate of tasks to accomplish and that human spaceflight is draining funds from more important missions. Other critics question the scientific value of sending people into space. Their argument is that human spaceflight is an expensive "stunt" and that scientific goals can be more easily and satisfactorily accomplished by robotic spacecraft.

But the actual experience of astronauts and cosmonauts over the past 38 years has decisively shown the merits of people as explorers of space. Human capability is required in space to install and maintain complex scientific instruments and to conduct field exploration. These tasks take advantage of human flexibility, experience and judgment. They demand skills that are unlikely to be automated within the foreseeable future. A program of purely robotic exploration is inadequate in addressing the important scientific issues that make the planets worthy of detailed study.

Many of the scientific instruments sent into space require careful emplacement and alignment to work properly. Astronauts have successfully deployed instruments in Earth orbit—for example, the Hubble Space Telescope—and on the sur-

Continued on page 6

ROBOTS

Slakey, continued from page 2

NASA is still conducting grade-A science in space, but it is being done by unmanned probes rather than astronauts. In recent years the Pathfinder rover has scoured the surface of Mars, and the Galileo spacecraft has surveyed Jupiter and its moons. The Hubble Space Telescope and other orbital observatories are bringing back pictures of the early moments of creation. But robots aren't heroes. No one throws a ticker-tape parade for a telescope. Human spaceflight provides the stories that NASA uses to sell its programs to the public. And that's the main reason NASA spends nearly a quarter of its budget to launch the space shuttle about half a dozen times each year.

The space agency has now started building the International Space Station, the long-planned orbiting laboratory. NASA says the station will provide a platform for space research and help determine how people can live and work safely in space. This knowledge could then be used to plan a manned mission to Mars or the construction of a base on the moon. But these justifications for the station are largely myths. Here are the facts, plain as potatoes: The International Space Station is not a platform for cutting-edge science. Unmanned probes can explore Mars and other planets more cheaply and effectively than manned missions can. And a moon colony is not in our destiny.

The Myth of Science

In 1990 the American Physical Society, an organization of 41,000 physicists, reviewed the experiments then planned for the International Space Station. Many of the studies involved examining materials and fluid mechanics in the station's microgravity environment. Other proposed experiments focused on growing protein crystals and cell cultures on the station. The physical society concluded, however, that these experiments would not provide enough useful scientific knowledge to justify building the station. Thirteen other scientific organizations, including the American Chemical Society and the American Crystallographic Association, drew the same conclusion.

Since then, the station has been redesigned and the list of planned experiments has changed, but the research community remains overwhelmingly opposed. To date, at least 20 scientific organizations from around the world have determined that the experiments in their respective fields are a waste of time and money. All

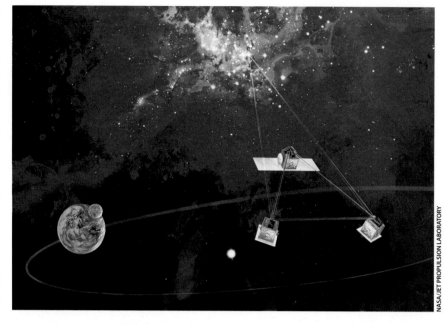

UNMANNED SPACECRAFT are becoming more versatile. In the Deep Space 3 mission, scheduled for launch in 2002, three vessels will fly in formation to create an optical interferometer, which will observe distant stars at high resolution. The spacecraft will fly between 100 meters and one kilometer apart.

these groups have recommended that space science should instead be done through robotic and telescopic missions.

These scientists have various reasons for their disapproval. For researchers in materials science, the station would simply be too unstable a platform. Vibrations caused by the movements of astronauts and machinery would jar sensitive experiments. The same vibrations would make it difficult for astronomers to observe the heavens and for geologists and climatologists to study Earth's surface as well as they could with unmanned satellites. The cloud of gases vented from the station would interfere with any experiments in space nearby that require near-vacuum conditions. And last, the station would orbit only 400 kilometers (250 miles) overhead, traveling through a region of space that has already been studied extensively.

Despite the scientific community's disapproval, NASA plans to go ahead with the proposed experiments on the space station. The agency has been particularly enthusiastic about studying the growth of protein crystals in microgravity; NASA claims the studies may spur the development of better medicines. But in July 1998 the American Society for Cell Biology bluntly called for the cancellation of the crystallography program. The

society's review panel concluded that the proposed experiments were not likely to make any serious contributions to the knowledge of protein structure.

The Myth of Economic Benefit

Human spaceflight is extremely expensive. A single flight of the space shuttle costs about $420 million. The shuttle's cargo bay can carry up to 23,000 kilograms (51,000 pounds) of payload into orbit and can return 14,500 kilograms back to Earth. Suppose that NASA loaded up the shuttle's cargo bay with confetti before launching it into space. Even if every kilogram of confetti miraculously turned into a kilogram of gold during the trip, the mission would still lose $270 million.

The same miserable economics hold for the International Space Station. Over the past 15 years the station has undergone five major redesigns and has fallen 11 years behind schedule. NASA has already spent nearly twice the $8 billion that the original project was supposed to cost in its entirety. The construction budget is now expected to climb above $40 billion, and the U.S. General Accounting Office estimates that the total outlay over the station's expected 10-year lifetime will exceed $100 billion.

NASA had hoped that space-based manufacturing on the station would offset some of this expense. In theory, the microgravity environment could allow the production of certain pharmaceuticals and semiconductors that would have advantages over similar products made on Earth. But the high price of sending anything to the station has dissuaded most companies from even exploring the idea.

NASA/JET PROPULSION LABORATORY

DEEP SPACE 4 mission will test the technologies for landing an unmanned probe on a comet. Slated for launch in 2003, the spacecraft will rendezvous with Comet Tempel 1, land a probe on the comet's nucleus and return drilling samples to Earth.

So far the station's only economic beneficiary has been Russia, one of America's partners in the project. Last year NASA announced plans to pay $660 million over four years to the Russian Space Agency so it can finish construction of key modules of the station. The money was needed to make up for funds the Russians could not provide because of their country's economic collapse. U.S. Congressman James Sensenbrenner of Wisconsin, who chairs the House Science Committee, bitterly referred to the cash infusion as "bailout money" for Russia.

But what about long-term economic benefits? NASA has maintained that the ultimate goal of the space station is to serve as a springboard for a manned mission to Mars. Such a mission would probably cost at least as much as the station; even the most optimistic experts estimate that sending astronauts to the Red Planet would cost tens of billions of dollars. Other estimates run as high as

$1 trillion. The only plausible economic benefits of a Mars mission would be in the form of technology spin-offs, and history has shown that such spin-offs are a poor justification for big-money space projects.

In January 1993 NASA released an internal study that examined technology spin-offs from previous missions. According to the study, "NASA's technology-transfer reputation is based on some famous examples, including Velcro, Tang and Teflon. Contrary to popular opinion, NASA created none of these." The report concluded that there have been very few technology-transfer successes at NASA over the past three decades.

The Myth of Destiny

Now it's time to get personal. When I was seven years old, I had a poster of the Apollo astronauts on my bedroom wall. My heroes had fearlessly walked on the moon and returned home in winged glory. They made the universe seem a bit smaller; they made my eyes open a bit wider. I was convinced that one day I would follow in their footsteps and travel to Mars.

So, what happened? I went to Mars three times—twice with the Viking landers in the late 1970s and the last time with the Mars Pathfinder mission in July 1997. I wasn't alone: millions of people joined me in front-row seats to watch Pathfinder's rugged Sojourner rover scramble over the Martian landscape. I've also traveled to Jupiter's moons with the Galileo spacecraft and seen hints of a liquid ocean on Europa. In 2004 I'll go to Saturn with the Cassini probe and get a close-up view of the planet's rings.

In recent years there have been tremendous strides in the capabilities of unmanned spacecraft. NASA's Discovery program has encouraged the design of compact, cost-effective probes that can make precise measurements and transmit high-quality images. Mars Pathfinder, for

example, returned a treasure trove of data and pictures for only $265 million. And NASA's New Millennium program is testing advanced technologies with spacecraft such as the Deep Space 2 microprobes. These two-kilogram instruments, now riding piggyback on the Mars Polar Lander spacecraft launched earlier this year, will plunge to the surface of Mars and penetrate up to two meters underground, where they will analyze soil samples and search for subsurface ice.

These spacecraft will still need human direction, of course, from scientists and engineers in control rooms on Earth. Unlike astronauts, mission controllers are usually not celebrated in the press. But if explorers Lewis and Clark were alive today, that's where they would be sitting. They would not be interested in spending their days tightening bolts on a space station.

Building a manned base on the moon makes even less sense. Unmanned spacecraft can study the moon quite efficiently, as the Lunar Prospector probe has recently shown. It is not our destiny to build a moon colony any more than it is to walk on our hands.

What's Next?

For the present, NASA appears committed to maintaining its human spaceflight program, whatever the cost. But in the next decade the space agency may discover that it does not need human characters to tell compelling stories. Mars Pathfinder proved that an unmanned mission can thrill the public just as much as a shuttle flight. The Pathfinder World Wide Web site had 720 million hits in one year. Maybe robots can be heroes after all.

Instead of gazing at posters of astronauts, children are now playing with toy models of the Sojourner rover. The next generation of space adventurers is growing up with the knowledge that one can visit another planet without boarding a spacecraft. Decades from now, when those children are grown, some of them will lead the next great explorations of the solar system. Sitting in hushed control rooms, they will send instructions to far-flung probes and make the final adjustments that point us toward the stars. 𝖲𝖠

Francis Slakey is an adjunct professor of physics at Georgetown University and associate director of public affairs for the American Physical Society. He received his Ph.D. in physics in 1992 from the University of Illinois, where his research focused on the optical properties of high-temperature superconductors. He writes and lectures on the subject of science policy; his commentaries have appeared in the *New York Times* and the *Washington Post*.

HUMANS

FUTURE ASTRONAUTS perform maintenance on a telescope on the moon's surface in this artist's conception. Humans are far more capable than robots in deploying scientific instruments and repairing complex equipment in space.

Spudis, continued from page 3

face of Earth's moon. In the case of the space telescope, the repair of the originally flawed instrument and its continued maintenance have been ably accomplished by space shuttle crews on servicing missions. From 1969 to 1972 the Apollo astronauts carefully set up and aligned a variety of experiments on the lunar surface, which provided scientists with a detailed picture of the moon's interior by measuring seismic activity and heat flow. These experiments operated flawlessly for eight years until shut down in 1977 for fiscal rather than technical reasons.

Elaborate robotic techniques have been envisioned to allow the remote emplacement of instruments on planets or moons. For example, surface rovers could conceivably install a network of seismic monitors. But these techniques have yet to be demonstrated in actual space operations. Very sensitive instruments cannot tolerate the rough handling of robotic deployment. Thus, the auto-deployed versions of such networks would very likely have lower sensitivity and capability than their human-deployed counterparts do.

The value of humans in space becomes even more apparent when complex equipment breaks down. On several occasions astronauts have been able to repair hardware in space, saving missions and the precious scientific data that they produce. When Skylab was launched in 1973, the lab's thermal heat shield was torn off and one of its solar panels was lost. The other solar panel, bound to the lab by restraining ties, would not release. But the first Skylab crew—astronauts Pete Conrad, Joe Kerwin and Paul Weitz—installed a new thermal shield and deployed the pinned solar panel. Their heroic efforts saved not only their mission but also the entire Skylab program.

Of course, some failures are too severe to be repaired in space, such as the damage caused by the explosion of an oxygen tank on the *Apollo 13* spacecraft in 1970. But in most cases when spacecraft equipment malfunctions, astronauts are able to analyze the problem, make on-the-spot judgments and come up with innovative solutions. Machines are capable of limited self-repair, usually by switching to redundant systems that can perform the same tasks as the damaged equipment, but they do not possess as much flexibility as people. Machines can be designed to fix expected problems, but so far only people have shown the ability to handle unforeseen difficulties.

Astronauts as Field Scientists

Exploration has two stages: reconnaissance and field study. The goal of reconnaissance is to acquire a broad overview of the compositions, processes and history of a given region or planet. Questions asked during the reconnaissance phase tend to be general—for instance, What's there? Examples of geologic reconnaissance are an orbiting spacecraft mapping the surface of a planet, and an automated lander measuring the chemical composition of the planet's soil.

The goals of field study are more ambitious. The object is to understand planetary processes and histories in detail. This requires observation in the field, the creation of a conceptual model, and the formulation and testing of hypotheses. Repeated visits must be made to the same geographic location. Field study is an open-ended, ongoing activity; some field sites on Earth have been studied continuously for more than 100 years and still provide scientists with important new insights. Field study is not a simple matter of collecting data: it requires the guiding presence of human intelligence. People are needed in the field to analyze the overabundant data and determine what should be collected and what should be ignored.

The transition from reconnaissance to field study is fuzzy. In any exploration, reconnaissance dominates the earliest phases. Because it is based on broad questions and simple, focused tasks, reconnaissance is the type of exploration best suited to robots. Unmanned orbiters can provide general information about the atmosphere, surface features and magnetic fields of a planet. Rovers can traverse the planet's surface, testing the physical and chemical properties of the soil and collecting samples for return to Earth.

But field study is complicated, interpretive and protracted. The method of solving the scientific puzzle is often not apparent immediately but must be formulated, applied and modified during the course of the study. Most important, fieldwork nearly always involves uncovering the unexpected. A surprising discovery may lead scientists to adopt new exploration methods or to make different observations. But an unmanned probe on a distant planet cannot be redesigned to observe unexpected phenomena. Although robots can gather significant amounts of data, conducting science in space requires *scientists*.

It is true that robotic missions are much less costly than human missions; I contend that they are also much less capable. The unmanned Luna 16, 20 and 24 spacecraft launched by the Soviet Union in the 1970s are often praised for returning soil samples from the moon at little cost. But the results from those missions are virtually incomprehensible without the paradigm provided by the results from the manned Apollo program. During the Apollo missions, the geologically trained astronauts were able to select the most representative samples of a given locality and recognize interesting or exotic rocks and act on such discoveries. In contrast, the Luna samples were scooped up indiscriminately by the robotic probes. We understand the geologic makeup and structure of each Apollo site in much greater detail than those of the Luna sites.

For a more recent example, consider the Mars Pathfinder mission, which was widely touted as a major success. Although Pathfinder discovered an unusual, silica-rich type of rock, because of the probe's limitations we do not know whether this composition represents an

igneous rock, an impact breccia or a sedimentary rock. Each mode of origin would have a widely different implication about the history of Mars. Because the geologic context of the sample is unknown, the discovery has negligible scientific value. A trained geologist could have made a field identification of the rock in a few minutes, giving context to the subsequent chemical analyses and making the scientific return substantially greater.

The Melding of Mind and Machine

Human dexterity and intelligence are the prime requirements of field study. But is the physical presence of people really required? Telepresence—the remote projection of human abilities into a machine—may permit field study on other planets without the danger and logistical problems associated with human spaceflight. In telepresence the movements of a human operator on Earth are electronically transmitted to a robot that can reproduce the movements on another planet's surface. Visual and tactile information from the robot's sensors give the human operator the sensation of being present on the planet's surface, "inside" the robot. As a bonus, the robot surrogate can be given enhanced strength, endurance and sensory capabilities.

If telepresence is such a great idea, why do we need humans in space? For one, the technology is not yet available. Vision is the most important sense used in field study, and no real-time imaging system developed to date can match human vision, which provides 20 times more resolution than a video screen. But the most serious obstacle for telepresent systems is not technological but psychological. The process that scientists use to conduct exploration in the field is poorly understood, and one cannot simulate what is not understood.

Finally, there is the critical problem of time delay. Ideally, telepresence requires minimal delays between the operator's command to the robot, the execution of the command and the observation of the effect. The distances in space are so vast that instantaneous response is impossible. A signal would take 2.6 seconds to make a round-trip between Earth and its moon. The round-trip delay between Earth and Mars can be as long as 40 minutes, making true telepresence impossible. Robotic Mars probes must rely on a cumbersome interface, which

forces the operator to be more preoccupied with physical manipulation than with exploration.

Robots and Humans as Partners

Currently NASA is focusing on the construction of the International Space Station. The station is not a destination, however; it is a place to learn how to roam farther afield. Although some scientific research will be done there, the station's real value will be to teach astronauts how to live and work in space. Astronauts must master the process of in-orbit assembly so they can build the complex vehicles needed for interplanetary missions. In the coming decades, the moon will also prove useful as a laboratory and test bed. Astronauts at a lunar base could operate observatories and study the local geology for clues to the history of the solar system. They could also use telepresence to explore the moon's inhospitable environment and learn how to mix human and robotic activities to meet their scientific goals.

The motives for exploration are both emotional and logical. The desire to probe new territory, to see what's over the hill, is a natural human impulse. This impulse also has a rational basis: by broadening the imagination and skills of the human species, exploration improves the chances of our long-term survival. Judicious use of robots and unmanned spacecraft can reduce the risk and increase the effectiveness of planetary exploration. But robots will never be replacements for people. Some scientists believe that artificial-intelligence software may enhance the capabilities of unmanned probes, but so far those capabilities fall far short of what is required for even the most rudimentary forms of field study.

To answer the question "Humans or robots?" one must first define the task. If space exploration is about going to new worlds and understanding the universe in ever increasing detail, then both robots and humans will be needed. The strengths of each partner make up for the other's weaknesses. To use only one technique is to deprive ourselves of the best of both worlds: the intelligence and flexibility of human participation and the beneficial use of robotic assistance. **SA**

Paul D. Spudis is a staff scientist at the Lunar and Planetary Institute in Houston. He earned his Ph.D. in geology from Arizona State University in 1982 and worked for the U.S. Geological Survey's astrogeology branch until 1990. His research has focused on the moon's geologic history and on volcanism and impact cratering on the planets. He has served on numerous committees advising NASA on exploration strategies and is the author of *The Once and Future Moon* (Smithsonian Institution Press, 1996).

Migrating Planets

by Renu Malhotra

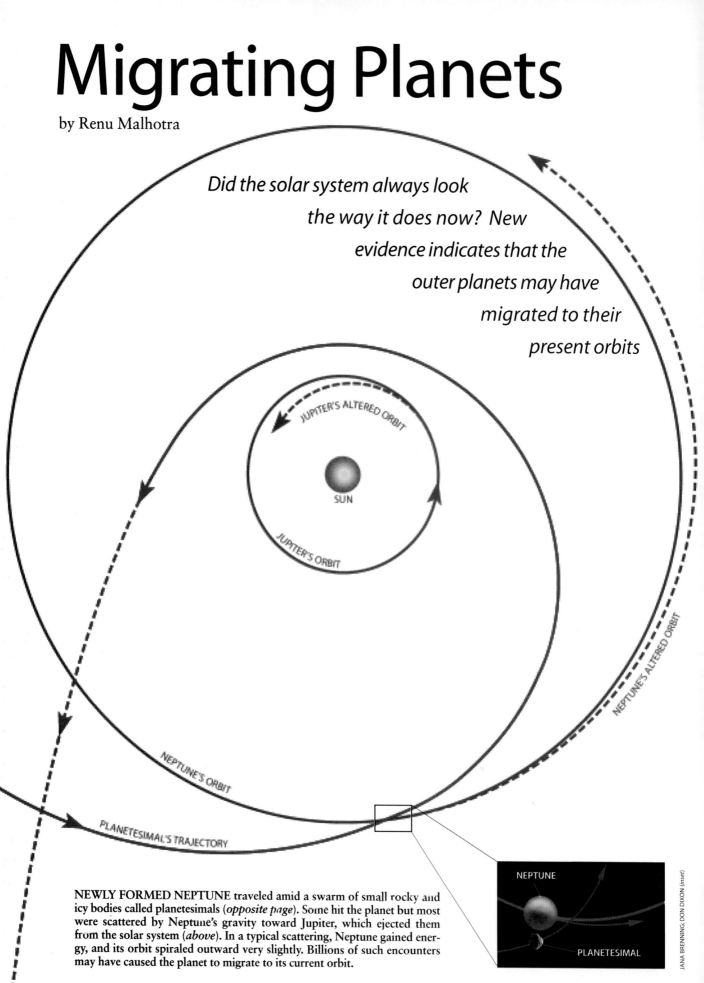

Did the solar system always look the way it does now? New evidence indicates that the outer planets may have migrated to their present orbits

JUPITER'S ALTERED ORBIT

SUN

JUPITER'S ORBIT

NEPTUNE'S ALTERED ORBIT

NEPTUNE'S ORBIT

PLANETESIMAL'S TRAJECTORY

NEPTUNE

PLANETESIMAL

NEWLY FORMED NEPTUNE traveled amid a swarm of small rocky and icy bodies called planetesimals (*opposite page*). Some hit the planet but most were scattered by Neptune's gravity toward Jupiter, which ejected them from the solar system (*above*). In a typical scattering, Neptune gained energy, and its orbit spiraled outward very slightly. Billions of such encounters may have caused the planet to migrate to its current orbit.

In the familiar visual renditions of the solar system, each planet moves around the sun in its own well-defined orbit, maintaining a respectful distance from its neighbors. The planets have maintained this celestial merry-go-round since astronomers began recording their motions, and mathematical models show that this very stable orbital configuration has existed for almost the entire 4.5-billion-year history of the solar system. It is tempting, then, to assume that the planets were "born" in the orbits that we now observe.

Certainly it is the simplest hypothesis. Modern-day astronomers have generally presumed that the observed distances of the planets from the sun indicate their birthplaces in the solar nebula, the primordial disk of dust and gas that gave rise to the solar system. The orbital radii of the planets have been used to infer the mass distribution within the solar nebula. With this

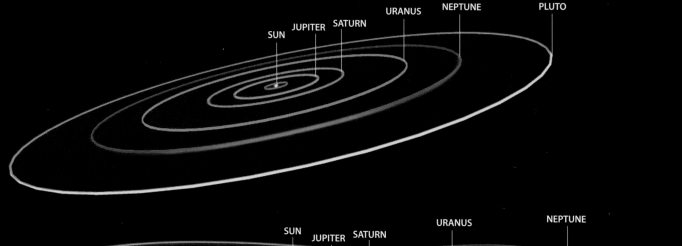

basic information, theorists have derived constraints on the nature and timescales of planetary formation. Consequently, much of our understanding of the early history of the solar system is based on the assumption that the planets formed in their current orbits.

It is widely accepted, however, that many of the smaller bodies in the solar system—asteroids, comets and the planets' moons—have altered their orbits over the past 4.5 billion years, some more dramatically than others. The demise of Comet Shoemaker-Levy 9 when it collided with Jupiter in 1994 was striking evidence of the dynamic nature of some objects in the solar system. Still smaller objects—micron- and millimeter-size interplanetary particles shaken loose from

comets and asteroids—undergo a more gradual orbital evolution, gently spiraling in toward the sun and raining down on the planets in their path.

Furthermore, the orbits of many planetary satellites have changed significantly since their formation. For example, Earth's moon is believed to have formed within 30,000 kilometers (18,600 miles) of Earth—but it now orbits at a distance of 384,000 kilometers. The moon has receded by nearly 100,000 kilometers in just the past billion years because of tidal forces (small gravitational torques) exerted by our planet. Also, many satellites of the outer planets orbit in lockstep with one another: for instance, the orbital period of Ganymede, Jupiter's largest moon, is twice that of Europa,

which in turn has a period twice that of Io. This precise synchronization is believed to be the result of a gradual evolution of the satellites' orbits by means of tidal forces exerted by the planet they are circling.

Until recently, little provoked the idea that the orbital configuration of the planets has altered significantly since their formation. But some remarkable developments during the past five years indicate that the planets may indeed have migrated from their original orbits. The discovery of the Kuiper belt has shown that our solar system does not end at Pluto. Approximately 100,000 icy "minor planets" (ranging between 100 and 1,000 kilometers in diameter) and an even greater number of smaller

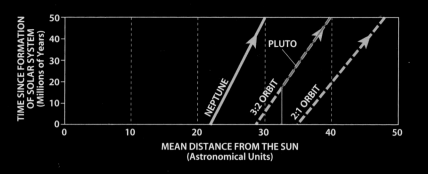

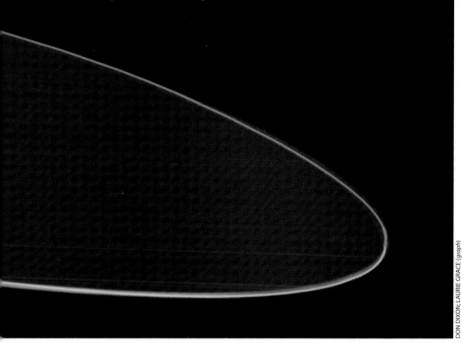

PLANETARY MIGRATION is shown in illustrations of the solar system at the time when the planets formed (*top left*) and in the present (*bottom left*). The orbit of Jupiter is believed to have shrunk slightly, while the orbits of Saturn, Uranus and Neptune expanded. (The inner planetary region was not significantly affected by this process.) According to this theory, Pluto was originally in a circular orbit. As Neptune migrated outward, it swept Pluto into a 3:2 resonant orbit, which has a period proportional to Neptune's (*above*). Neptune's gravity forced Pluto's orbit to become more eccentric and inclined to the plane of the other planets' orbits.

bodies occupy a region extending from Neptune's orbit—about 4.5 billion kilometers from the sun—to at least twice that distance. The distribution of these objects exhibits prominent nonrandom features that cannot be readily explained by the current model of the solar system. Theoretical models for the origin of these peculiarities suggest the intriguing possibility that the Kuiper belt bears traces of the orbital history of the gas-giant planets—specifically, evidence of a slow spreading of these planets' orbits subsequent to their formation.

What is more, the recent discovery of several Jupiter-size companions orbiting nearby sunlike stars in peculiarly small orbits has also focused attention on planetary migration. It is difficult to un-

derstand the formation of these putative planets at such small distances from their parent stars. Hypotheses for their origin have proposed that they accreted at more comfortable distances from their parent stars—similar to the distance between Jupiter and the sun—and then migrated to their present positions.

Pluto: Outcast or Smoking Gun?

Until just a few years ago, the only planetary objects known beyond Neptune were Pluto and its satellite, Charon. Pluto has long been a misfit in the prevailing theories of the solar system's origin: it is thousands of times less massive than the four gas-giant outer planets, and its orbit is very different

from the well-separated, nearly circular and co-planar orbits of the eight other major planets. Pluto's is eccentric: during one complete revolution, the planet's distance from the sun varies from 29.7 to 49.5 astronomical units (one astronomical unit, or AU, is the distance between Earth and the sun, about 150 million kilometers). Pluto also travels 8 AU above and 13 AU below the mean plane of the other planets' orbits [*see illustration at left*]. For approximately two decades in its orbital period of 248 years, Pluto is closer to the sun than Neptune is.

In the decades since Pluto's discovery in 1930, the planet's enigma has deepened. Astronomers have found that most Neptune-crossing orbits are unstable—a body in such an orbit will either collide with Neptune or be ejected from the outer solar system in a relatively short time, typically less than 1 percent of the age of the solar system. But the particular Neptune-crossing orbit in which Pluto travels is protected from close approaches to the gas giant by a phenomenon called resonance libration. Pluto makes two revolutions around the sun during the time that Neptune makes three; Pluto's orbit is therefore said to be in 3:2 resonance with Neptune's. The relative motions of the two planets ensure that when Pluto crosses Neptune's orbit, it is far away from the larger planet. In fact, the distance between Pluto and Neptune never drops below 17 AU.

In addition, Pluto's perihelion—its closest approach to the sun—always occurs high above the plane of Neptune's orbit, thus maintaining Pluto's long-term orbital stability. Computer simulations of the orbital motions of the outer planets, including the effects of their mutual perturbations, indicate that the relationship between the orbits of Pluto and Neptune is billions of years old and will persist for billions of years into the future. Pluto is engaged in an elegant cosmic dance with Neptune, dodging collisions with the gas giant over the entire age of the solar system.

How did Pluto come to have such a peculiar orbit? In the past, this question has stimulated several speculative and ad hoc explanations, typically involving planetary encounters. Recently, however, significant advances have been made in understanding the complex dynamics of orbital resonances and in identifying their Jekyll-and-Hyde role in producing both chaos and exceptional stability in the solar system. Drawing on this body

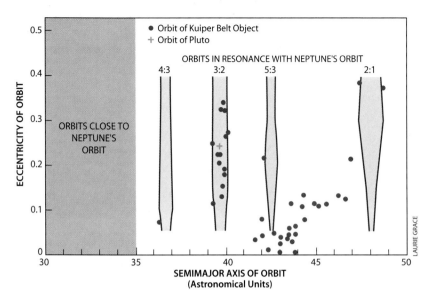

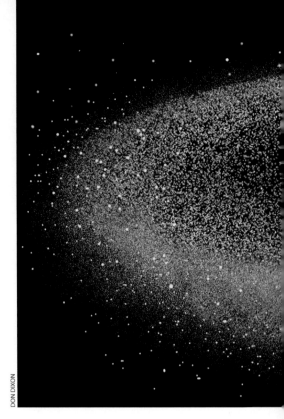

KUIPER BELT OBJECTS occupy a torus-shape region beyond Neptune's orbit (*right*). The theory of planetary migration predicts that concentrations of these objects would be found in orbits in resonance with Neptune's (*inside blue brackets in illustration above*). Recent observations indicate that about one third of the Kuiper belt objects for which orbits are known (*red dots*) are in 3:2 resonant orbits similar to Pluto's (*green cross*). Few objects are expected to be found in orbits that are very close to Neptune's (*shaded area*).

of knowledge, I proposed in 1993 that Pluto was born somewhat beyond Neptune and initially traveled in a nearly circular, low-inclination orbit similar to those of the other planets but that it was transported to its current orbit by resonant gravitational interactions with Neptune. A key feature of this theory is that it abandons the assumption that the gas-giant planets formed at their present distances from the sun. Instead it proposes an epoch of planetary orbital migration early in the history of the solar system, with Pluto's unusual orbit as evidence of that migration.

The story begins at a stage when the process of planetary formation was almost but not quite complete. The gas giants—Jupiter, Saturn, Uranus and Neptune—had nearly finished coalescing from the solar nebula, but a residual population of small planetesimals—rocky and icy bodies, most no larger than a few tens of kilometers in diameter—remained in their midst. The relatively slower subsequent evolution of the solar system consisted of the scattering or accretion of the planetesimals by the major planets [*see illustration on page 56*]. Because the planetary scattering ejected most of the planetesimal debris to distant or unbound orbits—essentially throwing the bodies out of the solar system—there was a net loss of orbital energy and angular momentum

from the giant planets' orbits. But because of their different masses and distances from the sun, this loss was not evenly shared by the four giant planets.

In particular, consider the orbital evolution of the outermost giant planet, Neptune, as it scattered the swarm of planetesimals in its vicinity. At first, the mean specific orbital energy of the planetesimals (the orbital energy per unit of mass) was equal to that of Neptune itself, so Neptune did not gain or lose energy from its gravitational interactions with the bodies. At later times, however, the planetesimal swarm near Neptune was depleted of the lower-energy objects, which had moved into the gravitational reach of the other giant planets. Most of these planetesimals were eventually ejected from the solar system by Jupiter, the heavyweight of the planets.

Thus, as time went on, the specific orbital energy of the planetesimals that Neptune encountered grew larger than that of Neptune itself. During subsequent scatterings, Neptune gained orbital energy and migrated outward. Saturn and Uranus also gained orbital energy and spiraled outward. In contrast, Jupiter lost orbital energy; its loss balanced the gains of the other planets and planetesimals, hence conserving the total energy of the system. But because Jupiter is so massive and had so much

orbital energy and angular momentum to begin with, its orbit decayed only slightly.

The possibility of such subtle adjustments of the giant planets' orbits was first described in a little-noticed paper published in 1984 by Julio A. Fernandez and Wing-Huen Ip, a Uruguayan and Taiwanese astronomer duo working at the Max Planck Institute in Germany. Their work remained a curiosity and escaped any comment among planet formation theorists, possibly because no supporting observations or theoretical consequences had been identified.

In 1993 I theorized that as Neptune's orbit slowly expanded, the orbits that would be resonant with Neptune's also expanded. In fact, these resonant orbits would have swept by Pluto, assuming that the planet was originally in a nearly circular, low-inclination orbit beyond Neptune. I calculated that any such objects would have had a high probability of being "captured" and pushed outward along the resonant orbits as Neptune migrated. As these bodies moved outward, their orbital eccentricities and inclinations would have been driven to larger values by the resonant gravitational torque from Neptune. (This effect is analogous to the pumping-up of the amplitude of a playground swing by means of small periodic pushes at the swing's natural frequency.) The final

Migrating Planets

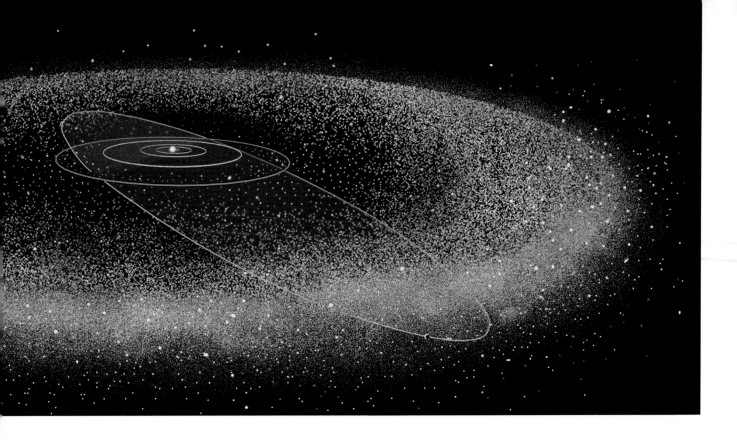

maximum eccentricity would therefore provide a direct measure of the magnitude of Neptune's migration. According to this theory, Pluto's orbital eccentricity of 0.25 suggests that Neptune has migrated outward by at least 5 AU. Later, with the help of computer simulations, I revised this to 8 AU and also estimated that the timescale of migration had to be a few tens of millions of years to account for the inclination of Pluto's orbit.

Of course, if Pluto were the only object beyond Neptune, this explanation of its orbit, though compelling in many of its details, would have remained unverifiable. The theory makes specific predictions, however, about the orbital distribution of bodies in the Kuiper belt, which is the remnant of the primordial disk of planetesimals beyond Neptune [see "The Kuiper Belt," by Jane X. Luu and David C. Jewitt; SCIENTIFIC AMERICAN, May 1996]. Provided that the largest bodies in the primordial Kuiper belt were sufficiently small that their perturbations on the other objects in the belt would be negligible, the dynamical mechanism of resonance sweeping would work not only on Pluto but on all the trans-Neptunian objects, perturbing them from their original orbits. As a result, prominent concentrations of objects in eccentric orbits would be found at Neptune's two strongest resonances, the 3:2 and the 2:1. Such orbits are ellipses with semimajor axes of 39.5 AU and 47.8 AU, respectively. (The length of the semimajor axis is equal to the object's average distance from the sun.)

More modest concentrations of trans-Neptunian bodies would be found at other resonances, such as the 5:3. The population of objects closer to Neptune than the 3:2 resonant orbit would be severely depleted because of the thorough resonance sweeping of that region and because perturbations caused by Neptune would destabilize the orbits of any bodies that remained. On the other hand, planetesimals that accreted beyond 50 AU from the sun would be expected to be largely unperturbed and still orbiting in their primordial distribution.

Fortunately, recent observations of Kuiper belt objects, or KBOs, have provided a means of testing this theory. More than 174 KBOs have been discovered as of mid-1999. Most have orbital periods in excess of 250 years and thus have been tracked for less than 1 percent of their orbits. Nevertheless, reasonably reliable orbital parameters have been determined for about 45 of the known KBOs [see illustration on opposite page]. Their orbital distribution is not a pattern of uniform, nearly circular, low-inclination orbits, as would be expected for a pristine, unperturbed planetesimal population. Instead one finds strong evidence of gaps and concentrations in the distribution. A large fraction of these KBOs travel in eccentric 3:2 resonant orbits similar to Pluto's, and KBOs in orbits interior to the 3:2 orbit are nearly absent—which is consistent with the predictions of the resonance sweeping theory.

Still, one outstanding question remains: Are there KBOs in the 2:1 resonance comparable in number to those found in the 3:2, as the planet migration theory would suggest? And what is the orbital distribution at even greater distances from the sun? At present, the census of the Kuiper belt is too incomplete to answer this question fully. But on Christmas Eve 1998 the Minor Planet Center in Cambridge, Mass., announced the identification of the first KBO orbiting in 2:1 resonance with Neptune. Two days later the center revealed that another KBO was traveling in a 2:1 resonant orbit. Both these objects have large orbital eccentricities, and they may turn out to be members of a substantial population of KBOs in similar orbits. They had previously been identified as orbiting in the 3:2 and 5:3 resonances, respectively, but new observations made last year strongly indicated that the original identifications were incorrect. This episode underscored the need for continued tracking of known KBOs in

A Planetary System at Last?

In April 1999 astronomer R. Paul Butler of the Anglo-Australian Observatory and his colleagues announced the discovery of what is apparently the first known case of a planetary system with several Jupiter-mass objects orbiting a sunlike star. (Previously, only systems with one Jupiter-mass companion had been detected.) The star is Upsilon Andromedae; it is approximately 40 light-years from our solar system and is slightly more massive and about three times more luminous than our sun.

The astronomers say their analysis of the observations shows that Upsilon Andromedae harbors three companions. The innermost object is at least 70 percent as massive as Jupiter and is moving in a nearly circular orbit only 0.06 AU—or about nine million kilometers—from the star. The outermost companion object is at least four times as massive as Jupiter and travels in a very eccentric orbit with a mean radius of 2.5 AU—half the radius of Jupiter's orbit. The intermediate object is at least twice as massive as Jupiter and has a moderately eccentric orbit with a mean radius of 0.8 AU.

If confirmed, the architecture of this system would pose some interesting challenges and opportunities for theoretical models of the formation and evolution of planetary systems. A number of

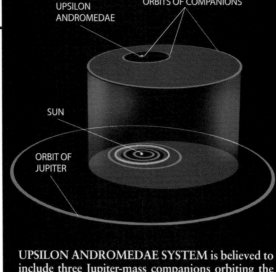

UPSILON ANDROMEDAE SYSTEM is believed to include three Jupiter-mass companions orbiting the star (*top*). Their theorized orbits are much tighter than Jupiter's orbit in our solar system (*bottom*).

dynamicists (including myself) have already determined that the orbital configuration of this putative system is at best marginally stable. The system's dynamical stability would improve greatly if there were no middle companion. This is noteworthy, as the observational evidence for the middle companion is weaker than that for the other two.

The Upsilon Andromedae system appears to contradict all the theorized mechanisms that would cause giant planets to migrate inward from distant birthplace orbits. If disk-protoplanet interactions caused the orbits to decay, the more massive planet would most likely be the earliest born and hence found at the shortest distance from the star—contrary to the pattern in the Upsilon Andromedae system. If only the innermost and outermost companions are real, the system could represent an example of the planet-planet scattering model in which two massive planets migrate to nearby orbits, then gravitationally scatter each other, eventually yielding one in a close, nearly circular orbit and the other in a distant, eccentric orbit. A difficulty with this scenario is that the more massive companion would be expected to evolve to the small orbit and the less massive one to the distant orbit—again, contrary to the characteristics of the Upsilon Andromedae system.

Could this system represent a hybrid case of these two scenarios—that is, orbital decay caused by disk-protoplanet interactions

---

order to map their orbital distribution correctly. We must also acknowledge the dangers of overinterpreting a still small data set of KBO orbits.

In short, although other explanations cannot be ruled out yet, the orbital distribution of KBOs provides increasingly strong evidence for planetary migration. The data suggest that Neptune was born about 3.3 billion kilometers from the sun and then moved about 1.2 billion kilometers outward—a journey of almost 30 percent of its present orbital radius. For Uranus, Saturn and Jupiter, the magnitude of migration was smaller, perhaps 15, 10 and 2 percent, respectively; the estimates are less certain for these planets because, unlike Neptune, they could not leave a direct imprint on the Kuiper belt population.

Most of this migration took place over a period shorter than 100 million years. That is long compared with the timescale for the formation of the planets—which most likely took less than 10 million years—but short compared with the 4.5-billion-year age of the so-

lar system. In other words, the planetary migration occurred in the early history of the solar system but during the later stages of planet formation. The total mass of the scattered planetesimals was about three times Neptune's mass. The question arises whether even more drastic orbital changes might occur in planetary systems at earlier times, when the primordial disk of dust and gas contains more matter and perhaps many protoplanets in nearby orbits competing in the accretion process.

Other Planetary Systems?

In the early 1980s theoretical studies by Peter Goldreich and Scott Tremaine, both then at the California Institute of Technology, and others concluded that the gravitational forces between a protoplanet and the surrounding disk of gas, as well as the energy losses caused by viscous forces in a gaseous medium, could lead to very large exchanges of energy and angular momentum between the protoplanet and the

disk. If the torques exerted on the protoplanet by the disk matter just inside the planet's orbit and by the matter just beyond it were slightly unbalanced, rapid and drastic changes in the planet's orbit could happen. But again, this theoretical possibility received little attention from other astronomers at the time. Having only our solar system as an example, planet formation theorists continued to assume that the planets were born in their currently observed orbits.

In the past five years, however, the search for extrasolar planets has yielded possible signs of planetary migration. By measuring the telltale wobbles of nearby stars—within 50 light-years of our solar system—astronomers have found evidence of more than a dozen Jupiter-mass companions in surprisingly small orbits around main-sequence stars. The first putative planet was detected orbiting the star 51 Pegasi in 1995 by two Swiss astronomers, Michel Mayor and Didier Queloz of the Geneva Observatory, who were actually surveying for binary stars.

in the case of the innermost object and mutual gravitational scattering for the other two companions? Perhaps entirely different formation and evolution processes are also involved, such as the fragmentation of the protostellar gas cloud that is thought to produce multiple-star systems and brown dwarf companions.

If only the innermost and outermost companions are real, the system would be architecturally similar to classic triple-stellar systems consisting of a tight binary with a distant third star in an eccentric orbit. At present, we have only speculations for the Upsilon Andromedae system. More observations and further analysis should help firm up the evidence for the number of companions and for their masses and orbital parameters.

The discovery methods employed so far are unable to detect planetary systems like our own because the stellar wobble from Earth-size planets in close orbits—or from Jupiter-size planets in more distant orbits—is below the observable threshold. Therefore, it would be premature to leap to conclusions about the astronomical frequency of Earth-like planets. Our understanding of the origin of the recently identified companions to sunlike stars is sure to evolve and thereby expand our understanding of our own solar system. —R.M.

Their observations were quickly confirmed by Geoffrey W. Marcy and R. Paul Butler, two American astronomers working at Lick Observatory near San Jose, Calif. As of June 1999, 20 extrasolar planetary candidates have been identified, most by Marcy and Butler, in search programs that have surveyed almost 500 nearby sunlike stars over the past 10 years. The technique used in these searches—measuring the Doppler shifts in the stars' spectral lines to determine periodic variations in stellar velocities—yields only a lower limit on the masses of the stars' companions. Most of the candidate planets have minimum masses of about one Jupiter-mass and orbital radii shorter than 0.5 AU.

What is the relationship between these objects and the planets in our solar system? According to the prevailing model of planet formation, the giant planets in our solar system coalesced in a two-step process. In the first step, solid planetesimals clumped together to form a protoplanetary core. Then this core gravitationally attracted a massive gaseous envelope from the surrounding nebula. This process must have been completed within about 10 million years of the formation of the solar nebula itself, as inferred from astronomical observations of the lifetime of protoplanetary disks around young sunlike stars.

At distances of less than 0.5 AU from a star, there is insufficient mass in the primordial disk for solid protoplanetary cores to condense. Furthermore, it is questionable whether a protoplanet in a close orbit could attract enough ambient gas to provide the massive envelope of a Jupiter-like planet. One reason is simple geometry: an object in a tight orbit travels through a smaller volume of space than one in a large orbit does. Also, the gas disk is hotter close to the star and hence less likely to condense onto a protoplanetary core. These considerations have argued against the formation of giant planets in very short-period orbits.

Instead several theorists have suggested that the putative extrasolar giant planets may have formed at distances of several AU from the star and subsequently migrated inward. Three mechanisms for planetary orbital migration are under discussion. Two involve disk-protoplanet interactions that allow planets to move long distances from their birthplaces as long as a massive disk remains.

With the disk-protoplanet interactions theorized by Goldreich and Tremaine, the planet would be virtually locked to the inward flow of gas accreting onto the protostar and might either plunge into the star or decouple from the gas when it drew close to the star. The second mechanism is interaction with a planetesimal disk rather than a gas disk: a giant planet embedded in a very massive planetesimal disk would exchange energy and angular momentum with the disk through gravitational scattering and resonant interactions, and its orbit would shrink all the way to the disk's inner edge, just a few stellar radii from the star.

The third mechanism is the scattering of large planets that either formed in or moved into orbits too close to one another for long-term stability. In this process, the outcomes would be quite unpredictable but generally would yield very eccentric orbits for both planets. In some fortuitous cases, one of the scattered planets would move to an eccentric orbit that would come so near the star at its closest approach that tidal friction would eventually circularize its orbit; the other planet, meanwhile, would be scattered to a distant eccentric orbit. All the mechanisms accommodate a broad range of final orbital radii and orbital eccentricities for the surviving planets.

These ideas are more than a simple tweak of the standard model of planet formation. They challenge the widely held expectation that protoplanetary disks around sunlike stars commonly evolve into regular planetary systems like our own. It is possible that most planets are born in unstable configurations and that subsequent planet migration can lead to quite different results in each system, depending sensitively on initial disk properties. An elucidation of the relation between the newly discovered extrasolar companions and the planets in our solar system awaits further theoretical and observational developments. Nevertheless, one thing is certain: the idea that planets can change their orbits dramatically is here to stay. SA

The Author

RENU MALHOTRA did her undergraduate studies at the Indian Institute of Technology in Delhi and received a Ph.D. in physics from Cornell University in 1988. After completing postdoctoral research at the California Institute of Technology, she moved to her current position as a staff scientist at the Lunar and Planetary Institute in Houston. In her research, she has followed her passionate interest in the dynamics and evolution of the solar system and other planetary systems. She also immensely enjoys playing with her four-year-old daughter, Mira.

Further Reading

NEWTON'S CLOCK: CHAOS IN THE SOLAR SYSTEM. Ivars Peterson. W. H. Freeman and Company, 1993.
DETECTION OF EXTRASOLAR GIANT PLANETS. Geoffrey W. Marcy and R. Paul Butler in *Annual Review of Astronomy and Astrophysics*, Vol. 36, pages 57–98; 1998.
DYNAMICS OF THE KUIPER BELT. Renu Malhotra et al. in *Protostars and Planets IV*. Edited by V. Mannings et al. University of Arizona Press (in press). Available at http://astro.caltech.edu/~vgm/ppiv/preprints.html on the World Wide Web.

Global Climate Change
on Venus

by Mark A. Bullock and David H. Grinspoon

*Venus's climate, like Earth's, has varied
over time—the result of newly appreciated connections
between geologic activity and atmospheric change*

NASA/JET PROPULSION LABORATORY

SURFACE OF VENUS was scanned by a radar system on board the Magellan space probe to a resolution of 120 meters (400 feet)—producing the most complete global view available for any planet, including Earth. A vast equatorial system of highlands and ridges runs from the continentlike feature Aphrodite Terra (*left of center*) through the bright highland Atla Regio (*just right of center*) to Beta Regio (*far right and north*). This image is centered at 180 degrees longitude. It has been drawn using a sinusoidal projection, which, unlike traditional map projections such as the Mercator, does not distort the area at different latitudes. Dark areas correspond to terrain that is smooth at the scale of the radar wavelength (13 centimeters); bright areas are rough. The meridional striations are image artifacts.

TOPOGRAPHY

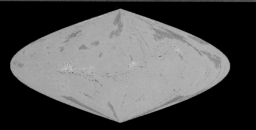

The topography of Venus spans a wide range of elevations, about 13 kilometers from low (*blue*) to high (*yellow*). But three fifths of the surface lies within 500 meters of the average elevation, a planetary radius of 6,051.9 kilometers. In contrast, topography on Earth clusters around two distinct elevations, which correspond to continents and ocean floors.

IMPACT CRATERS

Impact craters are randomly scattered all over Venus. Most are pristine (*white dots*). Those modified by lava (*red dots*) or by faults (*triangles*) are concentrated in places such as Aphrodite Terra. Areas with a low density of craters (*blue background*) are often located in highlands. Higher crater densities (*yellow background*) are usually found in the lowland plains.

TYPES OF TERRAIN

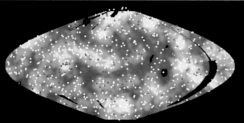

The terrain of Venus consists predominately of volcanic plains (*blue*). Within the plains are deformed areas such as tesserae (*pink*) and rift zones (*white*), as well as volcanic features such as coronae (*peach*), lava floods (*red*) and volcanoes of various sizes (*orange*). Volcanoes are not concentrated in chains as they are on Earth, indicating that plate tectonics does not operate.

AGES OF TERRAIN

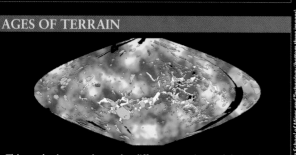

This geologic map shows the different terrains and their relative ages, as inferred from the crater density. Volcanoes and coronae tend to clump along equatorial rift zones, which are younger (*blue*) than the rest of the Venusian surface. The tesserae, ridges and plains are older (*yellow*). In general, however, the surface lacks the extreme variation in age that is found on Earth and Mars.

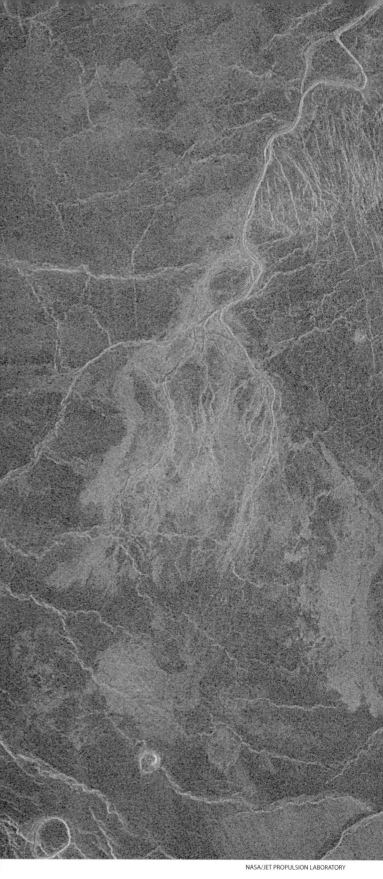

RIVER ON VENUS? This delta exists at the terminus of a narrow channel that runs for 800 kilometers through the northern volcanic plains. Water could not have carved it; Venus is too hot and dry. Instead it was probably the work of lavas rich in carbonate and sulfate salts—which implies that the average temperature used to be several tens of degrees higher than it is today. The region shown here is approximately 40 by 90 kilometers.

Global Climate Change on Venus

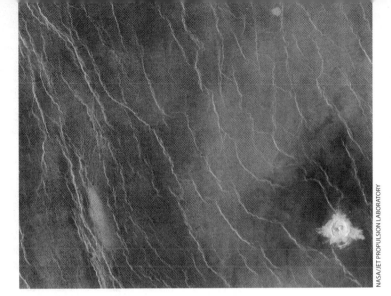

WRINKLE RIDGES are the most common feature on the volcanic plains of Venus. They are parallel and evenly spaced, suggesting that they formed when the plains as a whole were subjected to stress—perhaps induced by a dramatic, rapid change in surface temperature. This region, which is part of the equatorial plains known as Rusalka Planitia, is approximately 300 kilometers across.

Emerging together from the presolar cauldron, Earth and Venus were endowed with nearly the same size and composition. Yet they have developed into radically different worlds. The surface temperature of Earth's sister planet is about 460 degrees Celsius—hot enough for rocks to glow visibly to any unfortunate carbon-based visitors. A deadly efficient greenhouse effect prevails, sustained by an atmosphere whose major constituent, carbon dioxide, is a powerful insulator. Liquid water is nonexistent. The air pressure at the surface is almost 100 times that on Earth; in many ways it is more an ocean than an atmosphere. A mélange of gaseous sulfur compounds, along with what little water vapor there is, provides chemical fodder for the globally encircling clouds of sulfuric acid.

This depiction of hell has been brought to us by an armada of 22 robotic spacecraft that have photographed, scanned, analyzed and landed on Venus over the past 37 years. Throughout most of that time, however, Venus's obscuring clouds hindered a full reconnaissance of its surface. Scientists' view of the planet remained static because they knew little of any dynamic processes, such as volcanism or tectonism, that might have occurred there. The Magellan spacecraft changed that perspective. From 1990 to 1994 it mapped the entire surface of the planet at high resolution by peering through the clouds with radar [see "The Surface of Venus," by R. Stephen Saunders; SCIENTIFIC AMERICAN, December 1990]. It revealed a planet that has experienced massive volcanic eruptions in the past and is almost surely active today. Coupled with this probing of Venusian geologic history, detailed computer simulations have attempted to reconstruct the past billion years of the planet's climate history. The intense volcanism, researchers are realizing, has driven large-scale climate change. Like Earth but unlike any other planet astronomers know, Venus has a complex, evolving climate.

Earth's other neighbor, Mars, has also undergone dramatic changes in climate [see "Global Climate Change on Mars," by Jeffrey S. Kargel and Robert G. Strom; SCIENTIFIC AMERICAN, November 1996]. Its atmosphere today, however, is a relic of its geologic past. The interior of Mars is too cool now for volcanism to be active, and the surface rests in a deep freeze. Although variations in Mars's orbital and rotational motions can induce climate change there, volcanism will never again participate. Earth and Venus, on the other hand, have climates that are driven by the dynamic interplay between geologic and atmospheric processes.

From our human vantage point next door in the solar system, it is sobering to ponder how forces similar to those on Earth have had such a dissimilar outcome on Venus. Studying that planet has broadened research on climate evolution beyond the single example of Earth and given scientists new approaches for answering pressing questions: How unique is Earth's climate? How stable is it? Humankind is engaged in a massive, uncontrolled experiment on the terrestrial climate brought on by the growing effluent from a technological society. Discerning the factors that affect the evolution of climate on other planets is crucial to understanding how natural and anthropogenic forces alter the climate on Earth.

To cite one example, long before the ozone hole became a topic of household discussion, researchers were trying to come to grips with the exotic photochemistry of Venus's upper atmosphere. They found that chlorine reduced the levels of free oxygen above the planet's clouds. The elucidation of this process for Venus eventually shed light on an analogous one for Earth, whereby chlorine from artificial sources destroys ozone in the stratosphere.

Climate and Geology

The climate of Earth is variable partly because its atmosphere is a product of the ongoing shuffling of gases among the crust, the mantle, the oceans, the polar caps and outer space. The ultimate driver of geologic processes, geothermal energy, is also an impetus for the evolution of the atmosphere. Geothermal energy is a product primarily of the decay of radioactive elements in the interior, and a central problem in studying solid planets is understanding how they lose their heat. Two mechanisms are chiefly responsible: volcanism and plate tectonics.

The interior of Earth cools mainly by means of its plate tectonic conveyor-belt system, whose steady recycling of gases has exerted a stabilizing force on Earth's climate [see box on page 22]. Whereas volcanoes pump gases into the atmosphere, the subduction of lithospheric plates returns them to the interior. Most volcanoes are associated with plate tectonic activity, but some of the largest volcanic edifices on Earth (such as the Hawaiian Islands) have developed as "hot spots" independent of plate boundaries. Historically, the formation of immense volcanic provinces—regions of intense eruptions possibly caused by enormous buoyant plumes of magma within the underlying mantle—may have spewed large amounts of gases and led to periods of global warming [see "Large Igneous Provinces," by Millard F. Coffin and Olav Eldholm; Scientific American, October 1993].

What about Venus? Before the Magellan mission, much of the planet's geologic history remained speculative, relegated to comparisons with Earth and to extrapolations based on presumed similarities in composition and geothermal heat production. Now a global picture of the history of Venus's surface is emerging. Plate tectonics is not in evidence, except possibly on a limited scale. It appears that heat was transferred, at least in the relatively recent past, by the eruption of vast plains of basaltic lava and later by the volcanoes that grew on top of them. Understanding the effects of volcanoes is the starting point for any discussion of climate.

A striking feature of Magellan's global survey is the paucity of impact craters. Although Venus's thick atmosphere can shield the planet's surface from small impactors—it stops most meteoroids smaller than a kilometer in diameter, which would otherwise gouge craters up to 15 kilometers (nine miles) across—there is a shortage of larger craters as well. Observations of the number of asteroids and comets in the inner solar system, as well as crater counts on the moon, give a rough idea of how quickly Venus should have collected impact scars: about 1.2 craters per million years. Magellan saw only, by the latest count, 963 craters spread randomly over its surface. Somehow impacts from the first 3.7 billion years of the planet's history have been eradicated.

A sparsity of craters is also evident on Earth, where old craters are eroded by wind and water. Terrestrial impact sites are found in a wide range of altered states, from the nearly pristine bowl of Meteor Crater in Arizona to the barely discernible outlines of buried Precambrian impacts in the oldest continental crust. Yet the surface of Venus is far too hot for liquid water to exist, and surface winds are mild. In the absence of erosion, the chief processes altering and ultimately erasing impact craters should be volcanic and tectonic activity. That is the paradox. Most of the Venusian craters look fresh: only 6 percent of them have lava lapping their rims, and only 12 percent have been disrupted by folding and cracking of the crust. So where did all the old ones go, if most of those that remain are unaltered? If they have been covered up by lava, why do we not see more craters that are partially covered? And how have they been removed so that their initial random placement has been preserved?

To some researchers, the random distribution of the observed craters and the small number of partially modified ones imply that a geologic event of global proportions

abruptly wiped out all the old craters some 800 million years ago. In this scenario, proposed in 1992 by Gerald G. Schaber of the U.S. Geological Survey (USGS) and Robert G. Strom of the University of Arizona, impacts have peppered the newly formed surface ever since.

But the idea of paving over an entire planet is unpalatable to many geologists. It has no real analogue on Earth. Roger J. Phillips of Washington University proposed an alternative model the same year, known as equilibrium resurfacing, which hypothesized that steady geologic processes continually eradicate craters in small patches, preserving an overall global distribution that appears random. A problem with this idea is that some geologic features on Venus are immense, suggesting that geologic activity would not wipe craters out cleanly and randomly everywhere.

These two views grew into a classic scientific debate as the analysis of Magellan data became more sophisticated. The truth is probably somewhere in the middle. Elements of both models have been incorporated into the prevailing interpretation of the past billion years of Venus's geologic history: globally extensive volcanism wiped out most impact craters and created the vast volcanic plains 800 million years ago, and it has been followed by a reduced level of continued volcanic activity up to the present.

Chocolate-Covered Caramel Crust

Although there is no doubt that volcanism has been a major force in shaping Venus's surface, the interpretation of some enigmatic geologic features has until recently resisted integration into a coherent picture of the planet's evolution. Some of these features hint that the planet's climate may have changed drastically.

First, several striking lineaments resemble water-carved landforms. Up to 7,000 kilometers long, they are similar to meandering rivers and floodplains on Earth. Many end in outflow channels that look like river deltas. The extreme dryness of the environment makes it highly unlikely that water carved these features. So what did? Perhaps calcium carbonate, calcium sulfate and other salts are the culprit. The surface, which is in equilibrium with a hefty carbon dioxide atmosphere laced with sulfur gases, should be replete with these substances. Indeed, the Soviet Venera landers found that surface rocks are about 7 to 10 percent calcium minerals (almost certainly carbonates) and 1 to 5 percent sulfates.

Lavas laden with these salts melt at temperatures of a few tens to hundreds of degrees higher than Venusian surface temperatures today. Jeffrey S. Kargel of the USGS and his co-workers have hypothesized that vast reservoirs of molten carbonatite (salt-rich) magma, analogous to water

GREENHOUSE EFFECT

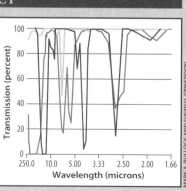

Greenhouse gases let sunlight reach the Venusian surface but block outgoing infrared light. Carbon dioxide (red), water (blue) and sulfur dioxide (yellow) each absorb a particular set of wavelengths. Were it not for these gases, the sunlight and infrared light would balance each other at a surface temperature of about −20 degrees Celsius (−4 degrees Fahrenheit).

MARK A. BULLOCK AND DAVID H. GRINSPOON

GAS CONCENTRATIONS

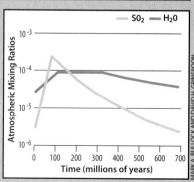

Water and sulfur dioxide are removed from the atmosphere after they are belched out by volcanoes. Sulfur dioxide (yellow) reacts relatively quickly with carbonates at the surface, whereas water (blue) is slowly broken apart by solar ultraviolet radiation.

MARK A. BULLOCK AND DAVID H. GRINSPOON

aquifers on Earth, may exist a few hundred meters to several kilometers under the surface. Moderately higher surface temperatures in the past could have spilled salt-rich fluid lavas onto the surface, where they were stable enough to carve the features we see today.

Second, the mysterious tesserae—the oldest terrain on Venus—also hint at higher temperatures in the past. These intensely crinkled landscapes are located on continentlike crustal plateaus that rise several kilometers above the lowland lava plains. Analyses by Phillips and by Vicki L. Hansen of Southern Methodist University indicate that the plateaus were formed by extension of the lithosphere (the rigid exoskeleton of the planet, consisting of the crust and upper mantle). The process was something like stretching apart a chocolate-covered caramel that is gooey on the inside with a thin, brittle shell. Today the outer, brittle part of the lithosphere is too thick to behave this way. At the time of tessera formation, it must have been thinner, which implies that the surface was significantly hotter.

Finally, cracks and folds crisscross the planet. At least some of these patterns, particularly the so-called wrinkle ridges, may be related to temporal variations in climate. We and Sean C. Solomon of the Carnegie Institution of Washington have argued that the plains preserve globally coherent episodes of deformation that may have occurred over short intervals of geologic history. That is, the entire lithosphere seems to have been stretched or compressed all at the same time. It is hard to imagine a mechanism internal to the solid planet that could do that. But what about global climate change? Solomon calculated that stresses induced in the lithosphere by fluctuations in surface temperature of about 100 degrees C (210 degrees Fahrenheit) would have been as high as 1,000 bars—comparable to those that form mountain belts on Earth and sufficient to deform Venus's surface in the observed way.

Around the time that the debate over Venus's recent geologic history was raging, we were working on a detailed model of its atmosphere. Theory reveals that the alien and hostile conditions are maintained by the complementary properties of Venus's atmospheric constituents. Water vapor, even in trace amounts, absorbs infrared radiation at wavelengths that carbon dioxide does not. Sulfur dioxide and other sulfur gases block still other infrared wavelengths [*see illustration below left*]. Together these greenhouse gases conspire to make the atmosphere of Venus partially transparent to incoming solar radiation but nearly completely opaque to outgoing thermal radiation. Consequently, the surface temperature (measured in kelvins) is three times what it would be without an atmosphere. On Earth, by comparison, the greenhouse effect currently

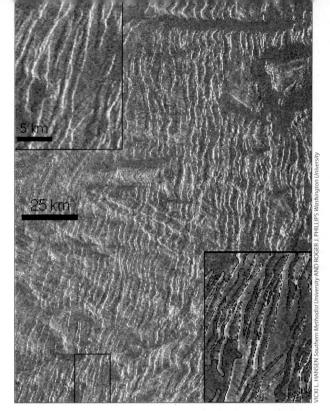

VICKI L. HANSEN Southern Methodist University AND ROGER J. PHILLIPS Washington University

RIBBON TERRAIN consists of steep-sided, flat-bottomed, shallow (400-meter) troughs. These features may have resulted from fracturing of a thin, brittle layer of rock above a weaker, ductile substrate. The insets show an enlargement of the region in the box, with the troughs marked on the bottom right.

boosts the surface temperature by only about 15 percent.

If volcanoes really did repave the Venusian surface 800 million years ago, they should have also injected a great deal of greenhouse gases into the atmosphere in a relatively short time. A reasonable estimate is that enough lava erupted to cover the planet with a layer one to 10 kilometers thick. In that case, the amount of carbon dioxide in the atmosphere would have hardly changed—there is already so much of it. But the abundances of water vapor and sulfur dioxide would have increased 10- and 100-fold, respectively. Fascinated by the possible implications, we modeled the planet's climate as an interconnected system of processes, including volcanic outgassing, cloud formation, the loss of hydrogen from the top of the atmosphere, and reactions of atmospheric gases with surface minerals.

The interaction of these processes can be subtle. Although carbon dioxide, water vapor and sulfur dioxide all warm the surface, the last two also have a countervailing effect: the production of clouds. Higher concentrations of water vapor and sulfur dioxide would not only enhance the greenhouse

CLOUD COVER

The sulfuric acid clouds vary in thickness after a global series of volcanic eruptions. The clouds first thicken as water and sulfur dioxide pour into the air. Then they dissipate as these gases thin out. About 400 million years after the onset of volcanism, the acidic clouds are replaced by thin, high water clouds.

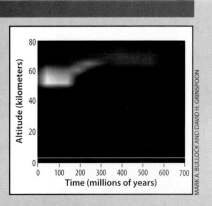

MARK A. BULLOCK AND DAVID H. GRINSPOON

TEMPERATURE

The surface temperature depends on the relative importance of clouds and the greenhouse effect. Initially volcanism produces thick clouds that cool the surface. But because water is lost more slowly from the planet's atmosphere than sulfur dioxide is, a greenhouse effect subsequently warms the surface.

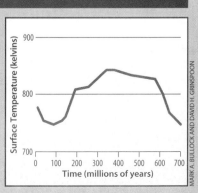

MARK A. BULLOCK AND DAVID H. GRINSPOON

Why Is Venus a Hellhole?

The stunning differences between the climates of Earth and Venus today are intimately linked to the history of water on these two worlds. The oceans and atmosphere of Earth currently have 100,000 times as much water as the atmosphere of Venus. Liquid water is the intermediary in reactions of carbon dioxide with surface rocks. Because of it, carbon dioxide in the air can form minerals. In addition, water mixed into the underlying mantle is probably responsible for the low-viscosity layer, or asthenosphere, on which Earth's lithospheric plates slide. The formation of carbonate minerals and their subsequent descent on tectonic plates prevent carbon dioxide from building up to the levels seen on Venus.

Yet models of planet formation predict that the two worlds should have been endowed with roughly equal amounts of water, delivered by the impact of icy bodies from the outer solar system. In fact, when the Pioneer Venus mission went into orbit in 1978, it measured the ratio of deuterium to ordinary hydrogen within the water of Venus's clouds. The ratio was an astonishing 150 times the terrestrial value [see "The Pioneer Mission to Venus," by Janet G. Luhmann, James B. Pollack and Lawrence Colin; Scientific American, April 1994]. The most likely explanation is that Venus once had far more water and lost it. Both the hydrogen and the deuterium, which are chemically equivalent, were tied up in water molecules. When water vapor drifted into the upper atmosphere, solar ultraviolet radiation decomposed it into oxygen and either hydrogen or deuterium. Because hydrogen, being lighter, escapes to space more easily than deuterium does, the relative amount of deuterium increased.

Why did this process occur on Venus but not on Earth? In 1969 Andrew P. Ingersoll of the California Institute of Technology showed that if the solar energy available to a planet were strong enough, any water at the surface would rapidly evaporate. The added water vapor would further heat the atmosphere and set up what he called the runaway greenhouse effect. The process would transport the bulk of the planet's water into the upper atmosphere, where it would ultimately be decomposed and lost. Later James F. Kasting of Pennsylvania State University and his co-workers developed a more detailed model of this effect [see "How Climate Evolved on the Terrestrial Planets," by James F. Kasting, Owen B. Toon and James B. Pollack; Scientific American, February 1988]. They estimated that the critical solar flux required to initiate a runaway greenhouse was about 40 percent larger than the present flux on Earth. This value corresponds roughly to the solar flux expected at the orbit of Venus shortly after it was formed, when the sun was 30 percent fainter. An Earth ocean's worth of water could have fled Venus in the first 30 million years of its existence.

A shortcoming of this model is that if Venus had a thick carbon dioxide atmosphere early on, as it does now, it would have retained much of its water. The amount of water that is lost depends on how much of it can rise high enough to be decomposed—which is less for a planet with a thick atmosphere. Furthermore, any clouds that developed during the process would have reflected sunlight back into space and shut off the runaway greenhouse.

So Kasting's group also considered the possibility of a solar flux slightly below the critical value. In this scenario, Venus had hot oceans and a humid stratosphere. The seas kept levels of carbon dioxide low by dissolving the gas and promoting carbonate formation. With lubrication provided by water in the asthenosphere, plate tectonics might have operated. In short, Venus possessed climate-stabilizing mechanisms similar to those on Earth today. But they were not foolproof. The atmosphere's lower density could not prevent water from diffusing to high altitudes. Over 600 million years, an ocean's worth of water vanished. Any plate tectonics shut down, leaving volcanism and heat conduction as the interior's ways to cool off. Thereafter carbon dioxide accumulated in the air.

This picture, termed the moist greenhouse, illustrates the intricate interaction of solar, climate and geologic change. Atmospheric and surface processes can reinforce one another and preserve the status quo, or they can conspire in their own destruction. If the theory is right, Venus once had oceans—perhaps even life, although it may be impossible to know for sure. —M.A.B. and D.H.G.

effect but also thicken the clouds, which reflect sunlight back into space and thereby cool the planet. Because of these competing effects, it is not obvious what the injection of the two gases did to the climate.

The Planetary Perspective

Our simulations suggest that the clouds initially won out, so that the surface cooled by about 100 degrees C. But then the clouds were slowly eaten away. Water diffused higher in the atmosphere, where it was dissociated by solar ultraviolet radiation. The hydrogen slowly escaped into space; half of it was lost within 200 million years. The sulfur dioxide, meanwhile, reacted with carbonate rocks. As laboratory experiments by Bruce Fegley, Jr., of Washington University and his co-workers have demonstrated, sulfur dioxide in Venus's atmosphere is taken up by carbonates much more quickly than water is lost to space.

As the clouds thinned, more solar energy reached the surface, heating it. After 200 million or so years, temperatures were high enough to start evaporating the clouds from below. A positive feedback ensued: the more the clouds eroded, the less sunlight was reflected back into space, the hotter the surface became, the more the clouds were evaporated from below, and so on. The magnificent cloud decks rapidly disappeared. For about 400 million years, all that remained of them was a wispy, high stretch of clouds composed mostly of water. Surface temperatures were 100 degrees C higher than at present, because the atmospheric abundance of water vapor was still fairly high and because the thin clouds contributed to the greenhouse effect without reflecting much solar energy. Eventually, about 600 million years after the onset of global volcanism, and in the absence of any further volcanic activity, the clouds would have dissipated completely.

Because sulfur dioxide and water vapor are continuously lost, clouds require ongoing volcanism for their maintenance. We calculated that volcanism must have been active within the past 30 million years to support the thick clouds observed today. The interior processes that generate surface volcanism occur over periods longer than tens of millions of years, so volcanoes are probably still active. This finding accords with observations of varying amounts of sulfur dioxide on Venus. In 1984 Larry W. Esposito of the University of Colorado at

Boulder noted that cloud-top concentrations of sulfur dioxide had declined by more than a factor of 10 in the first five years of the Pioneer Venus mission, from 1978 to 1983. He concluded that the variations in this gas and associated haze particles were a result of volcanism. Surface temperature fluctuations, precipitated by volcanism, are also a natural explanation for many of the enigmatic features found by Magellan.

Fortunately, Earth's climate has not experienced quite the same extremes in the geologically recent past. Although it is also affected by volcanism, the oxygen-rich atmosphere—provided by biota and plentiful water—readily removes sulfur gases. Therefore, water clouds are key to the planet's heat balance. The amount of water vapor available to these clouds is determined by the evaporation of the oceans, which in turn depends on surface temperature. A slightly enhanced greenhouse effect on Earth puts more water into the atmosphere and results in more cloud cover. The higher reflectivity reduces the incoming solar energy and hence the temperature. This negative feedback acts as a thermostat, keeping the surface temperature moderate over short intervals (days to years). An analogous feedback, the carbonate-silicate cycle, also stabilizes the abundance of atmospheric carbon dioxide. Governed by the slow process of plate tectonics, this mechanism operates over timescales of about half a million years.

These remarkable cycles, intertwined with water and life, have saved Earth's climate from the wild excursions its sister planet has endured. Anthropogenic influences, however, operate on intermediate timescales. The abundance of carbon dioxide in Earth's atmosphere has risen by a quarter since 1860. Although nearly all researchers agree that global warming is occurring, debate continues on how

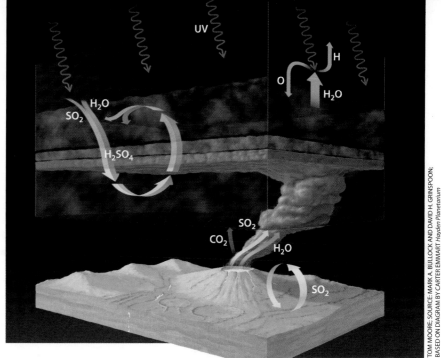

ATMOSPHERE OF VENUS suffers from ovenlike temperatures, oceanic pressures and sulfuric acid clouds (H_2SO_4). The reason is that Venus lacks the cycles that stabilize conditions on Earth. Its atmospheric processes are one-way. Carbon dioxide (CO_2), once injected by volcanoes, stays in the atmosphere; water (H_2O), once destroyed by ultraviolet light, is lost forever to the depths of space; sulfur dioxide (SO_2), once locked up in minerals, piles up on the surface (though a small amount does recycle).

much of it is caused by the burning of fossil fuels and how much stems from natural variations. Whether there is a critical amount of carbon dioxide that overwhelms Earth's climate regulation cycles is not known. But one thing is certain: the climates of Earth-like planets can undergo abrupt transitions because of interactions among planetary-scale processes [see box on page 22]. In the long run, Earth's fate is sealed. As the sun ages, it brightens. In about a billion years, the oceans will begin to evaporate rapidly and the climate will succumb to a runaway greenhouse. Earth and Venus, having started as nearly identical twins and diverged, may one day look alike.

We both recall the utopian view that science and technology promised us as children of the 1960s. Earth's capacity to supply materials and absorb refuse once seemed limitless. For all the immense change that science has wrought in the past few decades, one of the most powerful is the acquired sense of Earth as a generous but finite home. That perspective has been gained from the growing awareness that by-products from a global technological society have the power to alter the planetary climate [see "Global Warming Trends," by Philip D. Jones and Tom M. L. Wigley; SCIENTIFIC AMERICAN, August 1990]. Studying Venus, however alien it may seem, is essential to the quest for the general principles of climate variation—and thus to understanding the frailty or robustness of our home world. SA

The Authors

MARK A. BULLOCK and DAVID H. GRINSPOON are planetary scientists at the University of Colorado at Boulder. Bullock began his career studying the destruction of organic compounds on Mars and now analyzes the destruction of clement conditions on Venus. At night he takes his young sons, Sean and Brian, outside and shows them the points of light he studies. Grinspoon, in addition to studying the evolution of planetary atmospheres and of life, is a member of the Solar System Exploration Subcommittee, which advises NASA on space policy. He has played electric guitar and percussion in a variety of world-beat and trip-hop bands and lived in Zimbabwe for two months to learn chimurenga music.

Further Reading

THE STABILITY OF CLIMATE ON VENUS. Mark A. Bullock and David H. Grinspoon in *Journal of Geophysical Research,* Vol. 101, No. E3, pages 7521–7530; March 1996.
VENUS II: GEOLOGY, GEOPHYSICS, ATMOSPHERE, AND SOLAR WIND ENVIRONMENT. Edited by Stephen W. Bougher, Donald M. Hunten and Roger J. Phillips. University of Arizona Press, 1997.
VENUS REVEALED: A NEW LOOK BELOW THE CLOUDS OF OUR MYSTERIOUS TWIN PLANET. David H. Grinspoon. Perseus Books, 1997.
THE NEW SOLAR SYSTEM. Fourth edition. Edited by J. Kelly Beatty, Carolyn Collins Petersen and Andrew Chaikin. Cambridge University Press, 1998.
An interactive atlas of Venus is available at www.ess.ucla.edu/hypermap/ Vmap/top.html on the World Wide Web.

For student exercises relating to this article, please see the back of this reader

TOM MOORE; SOURCE: MARK A. BULLOCK AND DAVID H. GRINSPOON; BASED ON DIAGRAM BY CARTER EMMART *Hayden Planetarium*

The Mars Pathfinder

R ocks, rocks, look at those rocks," I exclaimed to everyone in the Mars Pathfinder control room at about 4:30 P.M. on July 4, 1997. The Pathfinder lander was sending back its first images of the surface of Mars, and everyone was focused on the television screens. We had gone to Mars to look at rocks, but no one knew for sure whether we would find any, because the landing site had been selected using orbital images with a resolution of roughly a kilometer. Pathfinder could have landed on a flat, rock-free plain. The first radio downlink indicated that the lander was nearly horizontal, which was worrisome for those of us interested in rocks, as most expected that a rocky surface would result in a tilted lander. The very first images were of the lander so that we could ascertain its condition, and it was not until a few tense minutes later that the first pictures of the surface showed a rocky plain—exactly as we had hoped and planned for.

Why did we want rocks? Every rock carries the history of its formation locked in its minerals, so we hoped the rocks would tell us about the early Martian environment. The two-part Pathfinder payload, consisting of a main lander with a multispectral camera and a mobile rover with a chemical analyzer, was suited to looking at rocks. Although it could not identify the minerals directly—its analyzer could measure only their constituent chemical elements—our plan was to identify them indirectly based on the elemental composition and the shapes, textures and colors of the rocks. By landing Pathfinder at the mouth of a giant channel where a huge vol-

Mission

*The first rover to explore Mars found in situ evidence that
the Red Planet may once have been hospitable to life*

by Matthew P. Golombek

U.S. GEOLOGICAL SURVEY AND NASA–JET PROPULSION LABORATORY; SUNSET SIMULATION BY LAURIE GRACE

TWILIGHT AT ARES VALLIS, Pathfinder's landing site, is evoked in this 360-degree panorama, a composite of a true sunset (*inset at left*) and other images. The rover is analyzing the rock Yogi to the right of the lander's rear ramp. Farther right are whitish-pink patches on the ground known as Scooby Doo (*closer to lander*) and Baker's Bench. The rover tried to scratch the surface of Scooby Doo but could not, indicating that the soil in these patches is cemented together. The much studied Rock Garden appears left of center. Flat Top, the flat rock in front of the garden, is covered with dust, but steep faces on other large rocks are clean; the rover analyzed all of them. (In this simulation, parts of the sky and terrain were computer-adjusted to complete the scene. During a real sunset, shadows would of course be longer and the ground would appear darker.) —*The Editors*

ume of water once flowed briefly, we sought rocks that had washed down from the ancient, heavily cratered highlands. Such rocks could offer clues to the early climate of Mars and to whether conditions were once conducive to the development of life [*see top illustration on page 28*].

The most important requirement for life on Earth (the only kind we know) is liquid water. Under present conditions on Mars, liquid water is unstable: because the temperature and pressure are so low, water is stable only as ice or vapor; liquid would survive for just a brief time before freezing or evaporating. Yet Viking images taken two decades ago show drainage channels and evidence for lakes in the highlands.

These features hint at a warmer and wetter past on Mars in which water could persist on the surface [*see "Global Climatic Change on Mars," by Jeffrey S. Kargel and Robert G. Strom; SCIENTIFIC AMERICAN, November 1996*]. To be sure, other explanations have also been suggested, such as sapping processes driven by geothermal heating in an otherwise frigid and dry environment. One of Pathfinder's scientific goals was to look for evidence of a formerly warm, wet Mars.

The possible lake beds are found in terrain that, judging from its density of impact craters, is roughly the same age as the oldest rocks on Earth, which show clear evidence for life 3.9 billion to 3.6 billion

NASA/JET PROPULSION LABORATORY

FIRST IMAGES

from Mars Pathfinder were assembled into this panorama of dark rocks, yellowish-brown dust and a butterscotch sky. Many rocks, particularly in the Rock Garden (*center*), are inclined and stacked—a sign that they were deposited by fast-moving water. About a kilometer behind the garden on the west-southwest horizon are the Twin Peaks, whose prominence identified the landing site on Viking orbiter images. After touching down, the lander pulled back the air bag and unfurled two ramps; the rover trundled down the rear ramp onto the surface the next day. (The small green and red streaks are artifacts of data compression.)

years ago. If life was able to develop on Earth at this time, why not on Mars, too, if the conditions were similar? This is what makes studying Mars so compelling. By exploring our neighboring planet, we can seek answers to some of the most important questions in science: Are we alone in the universe? Will life arise anywhere that liquid water is stable, or does the formation of life require something else as well? And if life did develop on Mars, what happened to it? If life did not develop, why not?

Pathfinding

Pathfinder was a Discovery-class mission—one of the National Aeronautics and Space Administration's "faster, cheaper, better" spacecraft—to demonstrate a low-cost means of landing a small payload and mobile vehicle on Mars. It was developed, launched and operated under a fixed budget comparable to that of a major motion picture (between $200 million and $300 million), which is a mere fraction of the budget typically allocated for space missions. Built and launched in a short time (three and a half years), Pathfinder included three science instruments: the Imager for Mars Pathfinder, the Alpha Proton X-ray Spectrometer and the Atmospheric Structure Instrument/Meteorology Package. The rover itself also acted as an instrument; it was used to conduct 10 technology experiments, which studied the abrasion of metal films on a wheel of the rover and the adherence of dust to a solar cell as well as other ways the equipment on

Pathfinder reacted to its surroundings.

In comparison, the Viking mission, which included two orbiter-lander pairs, was carried out more than 20 years ago at roughly 20 times the cost. Viking was very successful, returning more than 57,000 images that scientists have been studying ever since. The landers carried sophisticated experiments that tested for organisms at two locations; they found none.

The hardest part of Pathfinder's mission was the five minutes during which the spacecraft went from the relative security of interplanetary cruising to the stress of atmospheric entry, descent and landing [*see illustration on page 29*]. In that short time, more than 50 critical events had to be triggered at exactly the right times for the spacecraft to land safely. About 30 minutes before entry, the backpack-style cruise stage separated

SAND DUNES

provide circumstantial evidence for a watery past. These dunes, which lay in the trough behind the Rock Garden, are thought to have formed when windblown sand hopped up the gentle slope to the dune crest and cascaded down the steep side (which faces away from the rover in this image). Larger dunes have been observed from orbit, but none in the Pathfinder site. The discovery of these smaller dunes suggests that sand is more common on Mars than scientists had thought. The formation of sand on Earth is principally accomplished by moving water.

26 SCIENTIFIC AMERICAN PRESENTS

from the rest of the lander. At 130 kilometers above the surface, the spacecraft entered the atmosphere behind a protective aeroshell. A parachute unfurled 134 seconds before landing, and then the aeroshell was jettisoned. During descent, the lander was lowered beneath its back cover on a 20-meter-long bridle, or tether.

As Pathfinder approached the surface, its radar altimeter triggered the firing of three small solid-fuel rockets to slow it down further. Giant air bags inflated around each face of the tetrahedral lander, the bridle was cut, and the lander bounced onto the Martian surface at 50 kilometers per hour. Accelerometer measurements indicate that the air-bag-enshrouded lander bounced at least 15 times without losing air-bag pressure. After rolling at last to a stop, the lander deflated the air bags and opened to begin surface operations.

Although demonstrating this novel landing sequence was actually Pathfinder's primary goal, the rest of the mission also met or exceeded expectations. The lander lasted three times longer than its minimum design criteria, the rover 12 times longer. The mission returned 2.3 billion bits of new data from Mars, including more than 16,500 lander and 550 rover images and roughly 8.5 million individual temperature, pressure and wind measurements. The rover traversed a total of 100 meters in 230 commanded movements, thereby exploring more than 200 square meters of the surface. It obtained 16 measurements of rock and soil chemistry, performed soil-mechanics experiments and successfully completed the numerous technology experiments. The mission also captured the imagination of the public, garnering front-page headlines

for a week, and became the largest Internet event in history at the time, with a total of about 566 million hits for the first month of the mission—47 million on July 8 alone.

Flood Stage

The mosaic of the landscape constructed from the first images revealed a rocky plain (about 20 percent of which was covered by rocks) that appears to have been deposited and shaped by catastrophic floods [*see top illustration on opposite page*]. This was what we had predicted based on remote-sensing data and the location of the landing site (19.13 degrees north, 33.22 degrees west), which is downstream from the mouth of Ares Vallis in the low area known as Chryse Planitia. In Viking orbiter images, the area appears analogous to the Channeled Scabland in eastern and central Washington State. This analogy suggests that Ares Vallis formed when roughly the same volume of water as in the Great Lakes (hundreds of cubic kilometers) was catastrophically released, carving the observed channel in a few weeks. The density of impact craters in the region indicates it formed at an intermediate time in Mars's history, somewhere between 1.8 billion and 3.5 billion years ago.

The Pathfinder images support this interpretation. They show semirounded pebbles, cobbles and boulders similar to those deposited by terrestrial catastrophic floods. Rocks in what we dubbed the Rock Garden, a collection of rocks to the southwest of the lander, with the names Shark, Half Dome and Moe, are inclined and stacked, as if deposited by rapidly

flowing water. Large rocks in the images (0.5 meter or larger) are flat-topped and often perched, also consistent with deposition by a flood. Twin Peaks, a pair of hills on the southwest horizon, are streamlined. Viking images suggest that the lander is on the flank of a broad, gentle ridge trending northeast from Twin Peaks; this ridge may be a debris tail deposited in the wake of the peaks. Small channels throughout the scene resemble those in the Channeled Scabland, where drainage

> *By exploring our neighboring planet, we can seek answers to some of the most important questions in science.*

in the last stage of the flood preferentially removed fine-grained materials.

The rocks in the scene are dark gray and covered with various amounts of yellowish-brown dust. This dust appears to be the same as that seen in the atmosphere, which, as imaging in different filters and locations in the sky suggests, is very fine grained (a few microns in diameter). The dust also collected in wind streaks behind rocks.

Some of the rocks have been fluted and grooved, presumably by sand-size particles (less than one millimeter) that hopped along the surface in the wind. The rover's camera also saw sand dunes in the trough behind the Rock Garden [*see illustration below*]. Dirt covers the lower few centimeters of some rocks, suggesting that they have been exhumed by wind. Despite these signs of slow erosion by the wind, the rocks and surface appear to

U.S. GEOLOGICAL SURVEY

LANDING SITE
is an outflow channel carved by mammoth floods billions of years ago. It was chosen as the Pathfinder landing site for three reasons: it seemed safe, with no steep slopes or rough surfaces detected by the Viking orbiters or Earth-based radars; it had a low elevation, which provided enough air density for parachutes; and it appeared to offer a variety of rock types deposited by the floods. The cratered region to the south is among the oldest terrain on Mars. The ellipses mark the area targeted for landing, as refined several times during the final approach to Mars; the arrow in the larger inset identifies the actual landing site; the arrow in the smaller inset indicates the presumed direction of water flow.

have changed little since they were deposited by the flood.

The Alpha Proton X-ray Spectrometer on the rover measured the compositions of eight rocks. The silicon content of some of the rocks is much higher than that of the Martian meteorites, our only other samples of Mars. The Martian meteorites are all mafic igneous rocks, volcanic rocks that are relatively low in silicon and high in iron and magnesium. Such rocks form when the upper mantle of a planet melts. The melt rises up through the crust and solidifies at or near the surface. These types of rocks, referred to as basalts, are the most common rock on Earth and have also been found on the moon. Based on the composition of the Martian meteorites and the presence of plains and mountains that look like features produced by basaltic volcanism on Earth, geologists expected to find basalts on Mars.

The rocks analyzed by Pathfinder, however, are not basalts. If they are volcanic, as suggested by their vesicular surface texture, presumably formed when gases trapped during cooling left small holes in the rock, their silicon

content classifies them as andesites. Andesites form when the basaltic melt from the mantle intrudes deep within the crust. Crystals rich in iron and magnesium form and sink back down, leaving a more silicon-rich melt that erupts onto the surface. The andesites were a great

NASA/JET PROPULSION LABORATORY

SANDBLASTED ROCK
named Moe resembles terrestrial rocks known as ventifacts. Their fluted texture develops when sand-size particles hop along the surface in the wind and erode rocks in their path. On Earth, such particles are typically produced when water breaks down rocks. Moe's grooves all point to the northwest, which is roughly the same orientation as the grooves seen on other rocks at the site.

surprise, but because we do not know where these rocks came from on the Martian surface, we do not know the full implications of this discovery. If the andesites are representative of the highlands, they suggest that ancient crust on Mars is similar in composition to continental crust on Earth. This similarity would be difficult to reconcile with the very different geologic histories of the two planets. Alternatively, the rocks could represent a minor proportion of high-silicon rocks from a predominately basaltic plain.

Sedimentary Rocks?

Intriguingly, not all the rocks appear to be volcanic, judging by the diversity of morphologies, textures and fabrics observed in high-resolution images. Some rocks appear similar to impact breccias, which are composed of angular fragments of different materials. Others have layers like those in terrestrial sedimentary rocks, which form by deposition of smaller fragments of rocks in water. Indeed, rover images show many rounded pebbles and cobbles on the ground. In addition, some larger rocks have

Exploring Mars

what look like embedded pebbles and shiny indentations, where it looks as though rounded pebbles that were pressed into the rock during its formation have fallen out, leaving holes. These rocks may be conglomerates formed by flowing liquid water. The water would have rounded the pebbles and deposited them in a sand, silt and clay matrix; the matrix was subsequently compressed, forming a rock, and carried to its present location by the flood. Because conglomerates require a long time to form, if these Martian rocks are conglomerates (other interpretations are also possible) they strongly suggest that liquid water was once stable on the planet and that the climate was therefore warmer and wetter than at present.

Soils at the landing site vary from bright reddish dust to darker-red and darker-gray material, generally consistent with fine-grained iron oxides. Overall, the soils are lower in silicon than the rocks and richer in sulfur, iron and magnesium. Soil compositions are generally similar to those measured at the Viking sites, which are on opposite hemispheres (Viking 1 is 800 kilometers west of Pathfinder; Viking 2 is thousands of kilometers away on the opposite, eastern side of the northern hemisphere). Thus, the soil appears to include materials distributed globally on Mars, such as the airborne dust. The similarity in compositions among the soils implies that the variations in color at each site may be the result of slight differences in iron mineralogy or in particle size and shape

[*see top right illustration on next page*].

A bright reddish or pink material also covered part of the site. Similar to the soils in composition, it seems to be indurated or cemented because it was not damaged by scraping with the rover wheels.

Pathfinder also investigated the dust in the atmosphere of Mars by observing its deposition on a series of magnetic targets on the spacecraft. The dust, it turned out, is highly magnetic. It may consist of small silicate (perhaps clay) particles, with some stain or cement of a highly magnetic mineral known as maghemite. This finding, too, is consistent with a watery past. The iron may have dissolved out of crustal materials in water, and the maghemite may be a freeze-dried precipitate.

The sky on Mars had the same butter-

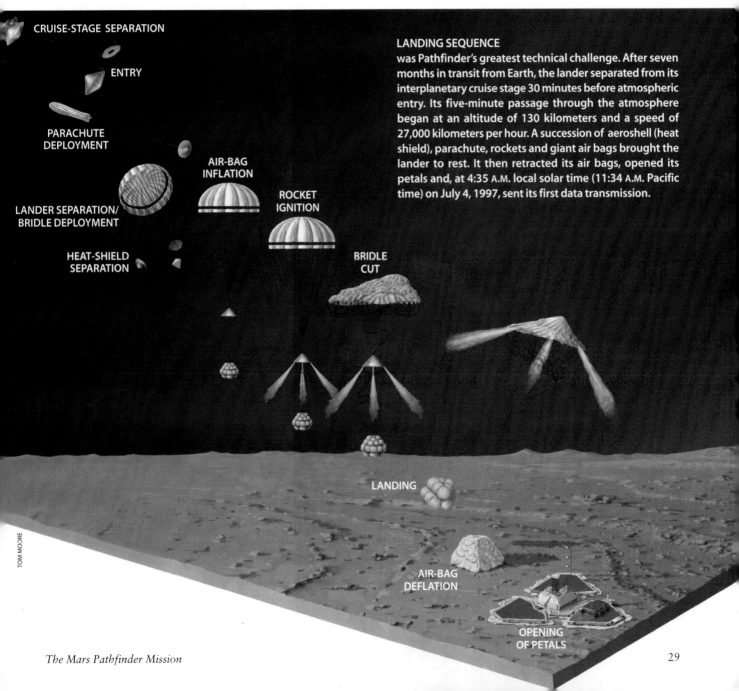

CRUISE-STAGE SEPARATION

ENTRY

PARACHUTE DEPLOYMENT

AIR-BAG INFLATION

ROCKET IGNITION

LANDER SEPARATION/ BRIDLE DEPLOYMENT

HEAT-SHIELD SEPARATION

BRIDLE CUT

LANDING SEQUENCE was Pathfinder's greatest technical challenge. After seven months in transit from Earth, the lander separated from its interplanetary cruise stage 30 minutes before atmospheric entry. Its five-minute passage through the atmosphere began at an altitude of 130 kilometers and a speed of 27,000 kilometers per hour. A succession of aeroshell (heat shield), parachute, rockets and giant air bags brought the lander to rest. It then retracted its air bags, opened its petals and, at 4:35 A.M. local solar time (11:34 A.M. Pacific time) on July 4, 1997, sent its first data transmission.

LANDING

AIR-BAG DEFLATION

OPENING OF PETALS

TOM MOORE

in the dawn sky, shown in this color-enhanced image taken on sol 39 (the 39th Martian day after landing), probably consist of water ice. During the night, water vapor froze around fine-grained dust particles; after sunrise, the ice evaporated. The total amount of water vapor in the present-day Martian atmosphere is paltry; if it all rained out, it would cover the surface to a depth of a hundredth of a millimeter. The basic appearance of the atmosphere is similar to what the Viking landers saw more than 20 years ago.

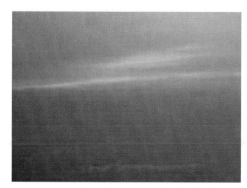

were exposed by the rover's wheels. The rover straddles Mermaid Dune, a pile of material covered by dark, sand-size granules. Its wheel tracks also reveal dark-red soil (*bottom left*) beneath the bright-reddish dust. Scientists were able to deduce the properties of surface materials by studying the effect that the wheels had on them.

PHOTOGRAPHS BY NASA/JET PROPULSION LABORATORY

scotch color as it did when imaged by the Viking landers. Fine-grained dust in the atmosphere would explain this color. Hubble Space Telescope images had suggested a very clear atmosphere; scientists thought it might even appear blue from the surface. But Pathfinder found otherwise, suggesting either that the atmosphere always has some dust in it from local dust storms or dust devils, or that the atmospheric opacity varies appreciably over a short time. The inferred dust-particle shape and size (a few microns in diameter) and the amount of water vapor in the atmosphere (equivalent to a pitiful hundredth of a millimeter of rainfall) are also consistent with measurements made by Viking. Even if Mars was once lush, it is now drier and dustier than any desert on Earth.

Freezing Air

The meteorological sensors gave further information about the atmosphere. They found patterns of diurnal and longer-term pressure and temperature fluctuations. The temperature reached its maximum of 263 kelvins (−10 degrees Celsius) every day at 2:00 P.M. local solar time and its minimum of 197 kelvins (−76 degrees C) just before sunrise. The pressure minimum of just under 6.7 millibars (roughly 0.67 percent of pressure at sea level on Earth) was reached on sol 21, the 21st Martian day after landing. On Mars the air pressure varies with the seasons. During winter, it is so cold that 20 to 30 percent of the entire atmosphere freezes out at the pole, forming a huge pile of solid carbon dioxide. The pressure

Summary of Evidence for a Warmer, Wetter Mars

Over the past three decades, scientists have built the case that Mars once looked much like Earth, with rainfall, rivers, lakes, maybe even an ocean. Pathfinder has added evidence that strengthens this case (*red*).

GEOLOGIC FEATURE	PROBABLE ORIGIN	IMPLICATION
Riverlike valley networks	Water flow out of ground or from rain	Either atmosphere was thicker (allowing rain) or geothermal heating was stronger (causing groundwater sapping)
Central channel ("thalweg") in broader valleys	Fluid flow down valley center	Valleys were formed by water flow, not by landslides or sapping
Lakelike depressions with drainage networks; layered deposits in canyons	Flow through channels into lake	Water existed at the surface, but for unknown time
Possible strand lines and erosional beaches and terraces	Possible shoreline	Northern hemisphere might have had an ocean
Rimless craters and highly eroded ancient terrain	High erosion rates	Water, including rain, eroded surface
Rounded pebbles and possible conglomerate rock	Rock formation in flowing water	Liquid water was stable, so atmosphere was thicker and warmer
Abundant sand	Action of water on rocks	Water was widespread
Highly magnetic dust	Maghemite stain or cement on small (micron-size) silicate grains	Active hydrologic cycle leached iron from crustal materials to form maghemite

LISA BURNETT

spacecraft show up as bright spots in these highly magnified images. The heat shield (*below*) fell about two kilometers southwest of the lander. The backshell (*right*) landed just over a kilometer to the southeast. These resting places and the location of the lander indicate that a breeze was blowing from the southwest.

NASA/JET PROPULSION LABORATORY

minimum seen by Pathfinder indicates that the atmosphere was at its thinnest, and the south polar cap its largest, on sol 21.

Morning temperatures fluctuated abruptly with time and height; the sensors positioned 0.25, 0.5 and one meter above the spacecraft took different readings. If you were standing on Mars, your nose would be at least 20 degrees C colder than your feet. This suggests that cold morning air is warmed by the surface and rises in small eddies, or whirlpools, which is very different from what happens on Earth, where such large temperature disparities do not occur. Afternoon temperatures, after the air has warmed, do not show these variations.

In the early afternoon, dust devils repeatedly swept across the lander. They showed up as sharp, short-lived pressure changes with rapid shifts in wind direction; they also appear in images as dusty funnel-shaped vortices tens of meters across and hundreds of meters high. They were probably similar to events detected by the Viking landers and orbiters and may be an important mechanism for raising dust into the Martian atmosphere. Otherwise, the prevailing winds were light (clocked at less than 36 kilometers per hour) and variable.

Pathfinder measured atmospheric conditions at higher altitudes during its descent. The upper atmosphere (altitude above 60 kilometers) was colder than Viking had measured. This finding may simply reflect seasonal variations and the time of entry: Pathfinder came in at 3:00 A.M. local solar time, whereas Viking arrived at 4:00 P.M., when the atmosphere is naturally warmer. The lower atmosphere was similar to that measured by

Viking, and its conditions can be attributed to dust mixed uniformly in comparatively warm air.

As a bonus, mission scientists were able to use radio communications signals from Pathfinder to measure the rotation of Mars. Daily Doppler tracking and less frequent two-way ranging during communication sessions determined the position of the lander with a precision of 100 meters. The last such positional measurement was done by Viking more than 20 years ago. In the interim, the pole of rotation has precessed—that is, the direction of the tilt of the planet has changed, just as a spinning top slowly wobbles. The difference between the two positional measurements yields the precession rate. The rate is governed by the moment of inertia of the planet, a function of the distribution of mass within the planet. The moment of inertia had been the single most important number about Mars that we did not yet know.

From Pathfinder's determination of the moment of inertia we now know that Mars must have a central metallic core that is between 1,300 and 2,400 kilometers in radius. With assumptions about the mantle composition, derived from the compositions of the Martian meteorites and the rocks measured by the

rover, scientists can now start to put constraints on interior temperatures. Before Pathfinder, the composition of the Martian meteorites argued for a core, but the size of this core was completely unknown. The new information about the interior will help geophysicists understand how Mars has evolved over time. In addition to the long-term precession, Pathfinder detected an annual variation in the planet's rotation rate, which is just what would be expected from the seasonal exchange of carbon dioxide between the atmosphere and the ice caps.

Taking all the results together suggests that Mars was once more Earth-like than previously appreciated. Some crustal materials on Mars resemble, in silicon content, continental crust on Earth. Moreover, the rounded pebbles and the possible conglomerate, as well as the abundant sand- and dust-size particles, argue for a formerly water-rich planet. The earlier environment may have been warmer and wetter, perhaps similar to that of the early Earth. In contrast, since floods produced the landing site 1.8 billion to 3.5 billion years ago, Mars has been a very un-Earth-like place. The site appears almost unaltered since it was deposited, indicating very low erosion rates and thus no water in relatively recent times.

Although we are not certain that early Mars was more like Earth, the data returned from Pathfinder are very suggestive. Information from the Mars Global Surveyor, now orbiting the Red Planet, should help answer this crucial question about our neighboring world. **SA**

Matthew P. Golombek is project scientist of Mars Pathfinder, with responsibility for the overall scientific content of the mission. He conducts his work at the Jet Propulsion Laboratory in Pasadena, Calif. He is chair of the Pathfinder Project Science Group, deputy of the Experiment Operations Team and a member of the project management group. He has written numerous papers on the spacecraft and its results and has organized press conferences and scientific meetings. Golombek's research focuses on the structural geology and tectonics of Earth and the other planets, particularly Mars. This article updates a version that appeared in the July 1998 issue of *Scientific American*.

For student exercises relating to this article, please see the back of this reader

The Hidden Ocean of

Doodles and freckles, creamy plains
and crypto-icebergs—the amazing surface
of Jupiter's brightest icy moon
hints at a global sea underneath

by Robert T. Pappalardo, James W. Head and Ronald Greeley

D o living things flourish elsewhere within our solar system, or is Earth's environment uniquely nurturing? This question is central to planetary exploration today. Three decades into humankind's reconnaissance of the planets and their natural satellites, only a short list of possible abodes remains. Perhaps the most intriguing is Jupiter's ice-rich moon Europa.

For centuries, astronomers knew Europa only as a pinprick of light in even the most powerful telescopes. In the 1960s spectroscopy showed that the satellite, like many others in the cold reaches of the outer solar system, is covered with ice. With surface temperatures of 110 kelvins (–260 degrees Fahrenheit) near the equator and 50 kelvins near the poles, that ice must form a rock-hard skin. Researchers had no way to probe deeper and little reason to expect anything special. But in the past two decades and especially in the past few years, spectacular images radioed from visiting spacecraft have revealed a young and tremendously deformed surface. Somewhere under the icy shell, it seems, must be a warm, mobile interior. Is it glacial ice? Or are Europa's innards warm enough to sustain an ocean of liquid water? If the latter, we can stretch our imaginations and ask whether life might have arisen within the lightless depths.

Planetary scientists have been trying to infer what lies inside Europa ever since the two Voyager spacecraft flew by Jupiter and its companions in 1979 [see "The Galilean Moons of Jupiter," by Laurence A. Soderblom; SCIENTIFIC AMERICAN, January 1980]. Celestial mechanics dictated that these spacecraft could pass by Europa only distantly. The photographs they did obtain were nonetheless tantalizing. Europa looked like a ball of string, its bright plains crisscrossed with bands and ridges. Researchers noticed that some dark wedge-shaped bands have opposing sides that match each other perfectly. Somehow the bright icy surface has been wrenched apart, exposing dark material that was fluid enough to permeate the ensuing void. These features resemble liquid-filled openings between floating plates of sea ice on Earth.

Unexpectedly, the Voyagers found very few large impact craters on Europa. A planetary surface slowly accumulates impact craters as it is occasionally hit by cometary and asteroidal debris. If Europa all but lacks visible craters, it must have been repaved by volcanic or tectonic events in the relatively recent past. Based on the number of comets with Jupiter-crossing orbits, the late cratering expert Eugene Shoemaker deduced that a crater larger than 10 kilometers (six miles) in diameter should form

Ocean of

EUROPA'S ICY COUNTENANCE resembles a cracked eggshell. Reddish material has oozed out of fractures opened up by Jupiter's gravitational forces. Very few craters are present, indicating that the surface is geologically young. On this Galileo spacecraft image, the colors are exaggerated but real. Other spacecraft instruments have found that Europa's interior is mainly rock, with an outer layer of water (in either liquid or solid form) about 100 kilometers thick (*bottom right*). Most of that water must be fluid or semifluid to account for surface features, such as the circular mounds pushed up by rising blobs of relatively hot ice (*far right*), which occasionally puncture the surface.

Europa

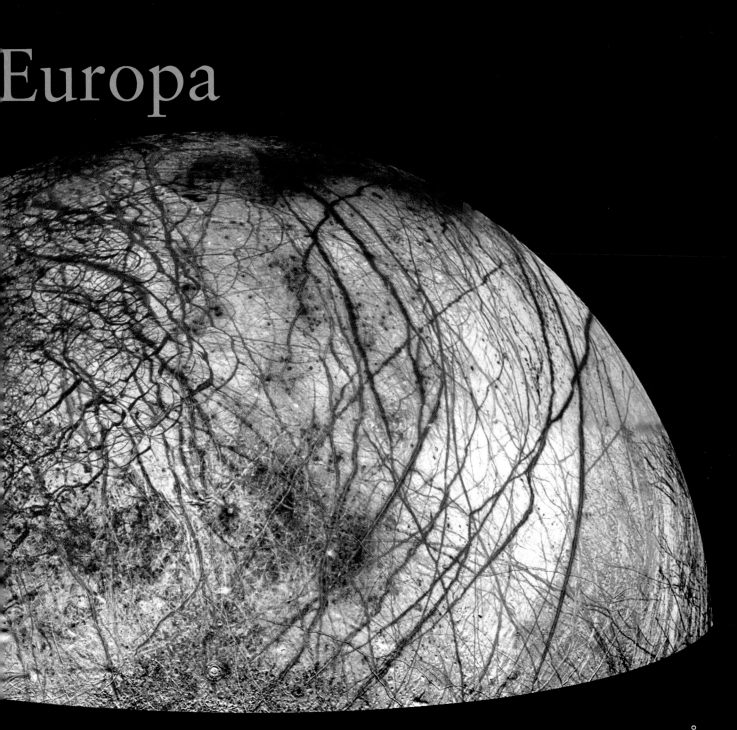

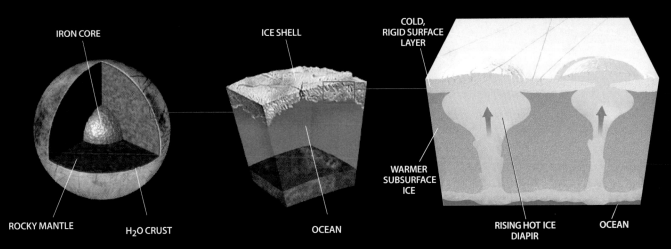

IRON CORE

ICE SHELL

COLD, RIGID SURFACE LAYER

WARMER SUBSURFACE ICE

ROCKY MANTLE

H₂O CRUST

OCEAN

RISING HOT ICE DIAPIR

OCEAN

EUROPA

100 KILOMETERS

NASA/JET PROPULSION LABORATORY; ALFRED T. KAMAJIAN (bottom left)

once every 1.5 million years on average. Extrapolation from the few known Europan craters suggested that 45 of this size might exist across the satellite, indicating a surface age of just 30 million years—a geological eyeblink. Shoemaker added that Europa's large craters might have flattened out over time if the interior were warm. The satellite could be active even today.

But this hypothesis remained uncertain. The Voyager images were too coarse to pick out smaller craters. Indeed, intermingled with the bright plains is mottled terrain filled with dark spots, mounds and pits. Some researchers pointed out that craters could be hiding in these odd regions, in which case the satellite's surface would be ancient. Besides, how

could a moon so small possibly be active? Similarly sized bodies, such as Earth's moon, are inert balls of rock, having lost most of their internal radioactively generated heat long ago. By all rights, Europa should now be cold and dead.

The Paper Clip Moons

Then researchers came to appreciate the power of an exotic heat source: tidal kneading, the process that drives volcanism on Europa's pizza-colored neighbor Io. Of the four large moons of Jupiter—Io, Europa, Ganymede and Callisto, collectively known as the Galilean satellites in honor of their

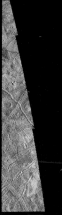
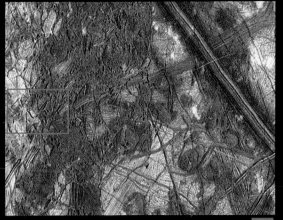

Simulated view of icy blocks, roughly three kilometers from side to side

GIANT BLOCKS OF ICE the size of a small city are progressively revealed in this sequence of Galileo images. A colossal X formed by two ridges (*first three images in top row*) helpfully marks the spot as the pictures zoom in on a dark splotch known as Conamara Chaos (*next two images*) and thence to individual iceberglike blocks (*above*). Warm ice, slush or liquid water once filled the low-lying "sea" in which the blocks sit, now frozen in place. An artist's impression (*left*), simulating a vantage point a few hundred meters above the surface looking south (*arrow in above image*), shows dirt tumbling downslope as fine ice particles slowly evaporate away.

discoverer—the first three are engaged in an elegant orbital dance called the Laplace resonance. With clockwork precision, each time Ganymede orbits Jupiter once (with a period of 7.2 Earth days), Europa orbits twice (3.6 days) and Io four times (1.8 days). The consequent gravitational push and pull distorts their orbits into oblong ellipses. They move nearer to, then farther from, their parent planet during each orbital revolution. In response, tides are raised and lowered in the body of each satellite. Like bending a paper clip rapidly back and forth, this tidal flexing generates heat [*see bottom illustration on page 39*].

The effects are felt most profoundly on Io, which is the closest to Jupiter. The interior temperature rises to the melting point of rock, powering continual volcanic eruptions. Europa, farther away, is heated less intensely. But the latest calculations indicate that its interior might be kept warm enough to melt ice below a depth of 10 to 30 kilometers, maintaining a global subsurface ocean.

After Voyager, observational tests of the ocean hypothesis had to wait nearly 20 years, until the worlds of Galileo could be visited by the spacecraft named for him. That spacecraft swung into orbit around Jupiter in December 1995. Every few months since then, its trajectory has brought it speeding closely past one of the Galilean satellites—including, a dozen times, Europa.

Even if Galileo had not sent back a single picture, it would have provided a vital insight. On each flyby, engineers and scientists have carefully tracked the spacecraft's radio signal in order to measure Europa's gravitational field. Any rotating and tidally distorted moon is slightly flattened, or oblate, so its gravitational field is also nonspherical. The irregular force causes slight shifts in the frequency of Galileo's signal, from which researchers have quantified the satellite's oblateness and, in turn, its internal mass distribution. (For a given rotation rate, a satellite with a more centrally concentrated mass will be less oblate than a homogeneous satellite.)

Tapestries and Hydraulic Bearings

Judging from its average density of 3.04 grams per cubic centimeter, Europa is predominantly a rocky object. The gravity data indicated that the rock is sandwiched between a central iron core and an outer crust of H_2O. Considering the likely range in density values for the iron core and rocky mantle, the water crust is between 80 and 170 kilometers thick, most likely about 100 kilometers. If a significant portion of it is liquid, its volume exceeds that of all the oceans of Earth combined. But Galileo's gravity data cannot tell whether this water layer is completely solid or partially liquid.

To address that question, one must look at the pictures. The Galileo imaging team found a world like no other. Its surface is an elaborate weave of fractures, ridges, bands and spots. The fractures presumably formed as tidal forces distorted the icy surface until it cracked. Ridges are similarly ubiquitous. They slice across the surface in pairs, each with a narrow valley down the center. Plausible models for their formation invoke the rise of liquid water or warm glacial ice along fractures. A watery or icy "magma" might have forced the rigid near-surface ice upward, warping it into a double ridge. Or an icy slurry might have erupted onto the surface to build each ridge. Multiple parallel ridges also occur, indicating that the process can repeat to create ridges side by side. The widest ones are commonly flanked by dark, reddish, diffuse-edged stripes. Perhaps the heat pulse associated with ridge formation created these darkened margins through icy volcanism or sublimation of a dirty ice surface. Whatever their exact formation mechanism, ridges point to a dynamic geological history and warm subsurface.

From the seemingly random doodlings of fractures and ridges, scientists have attempted to understand the manner in which Europa has been stretched and distorted. Tidal kneading produces a distinctive pattern, and some of Europa's freshest cracks and ridges fit that pattern. But something else must also have been going on. Strangely, it appears that the stress pattern has swept across the surface over time.

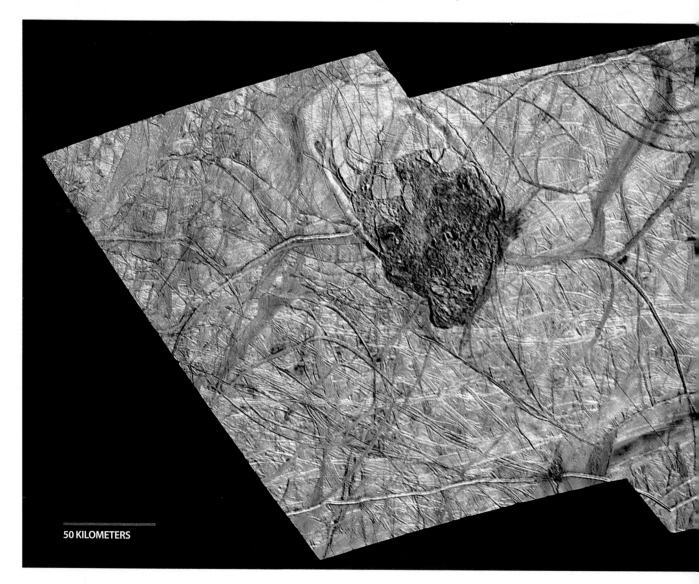

50 KILOMETERS

The Hidden Ocean of Europa

In fact, the pattern can be explained if Europa's surface has rotated faster than its interior. Most of the solar system's natural satellites are in synchronous rotation: torqued by tidal forces, they come to rotate exactly once for each orbital revolution, always showing the same face to their parent planet. (This is why we always see the same side of our moon from Earth and so speak of the moon's "far" side.) But if Europa's icy surface were decoupled—mechanically separated—from its rocky mantle, Jupiter's gravity would cause the surface to spin slightly faster than the synchronous rate. A subsurface ocean could easily act as such a bearing, allowing the floating ice shell to rotate nonsynchronously.

It cannot be said with certainty whether nonsynchronous rotation is going on today or whether the surface instead records an ancient pattern of now inactive lineaments. Scientists have compared the locations of features in Galileo images to their locations in Voyager images and found no measurable change over that 20-year period. Relative to the interior, the surface today cannot be rotating faster than once every 10,000 years.

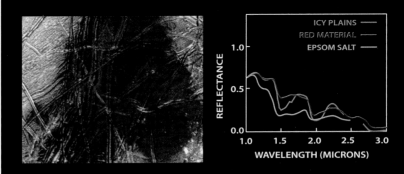

RUDDY SPOT marks where briny liquid poured out onto Europa's surface (*left*). Spectral measurements (*right*) found that surrounding bright plains (*blue*) consist mainly of water ice. The ruddy material (*red*) more nearly matches the laboratory spectrum of magnesium sulfate (*yellow*).

LEATHERY EXOSKELETON represented by chaos terrain on Europa is one of the strangest landscapes in the solar system. The Thera region (*left half of mosaic*) contains bright, dislodged plates of ice. The Thrace region (*right half*) is elongated, hummocky and higher in elevation. It spills into a gray band, Libya Linea, to the south. Such chaos regions might have formed when an underground ocean melted through the moon's icy shell or when upwelling blobs of warm ice disrupted the surface.

NASA/JET PROPULSION LABORATORY: CYNTHIA PHILLIPS *University of Arizona*

NASA/JET PROPULSION LABORATORY (*left*): SARAH DONELSON; SOURCE: THOMAS B. McCORD *University of Hawaii* (*right*)

Galileo's camera has also homed in on the dark wedge-shaped bands, where low-resolution Voyager images hinted that the ridged plains have pulled completely apart. Recent analyses have confirmed that the opposing sides of these bands are perfectly matched. The dark material in between is finely striated, commonly having a prominent central groove and some degree of symmetry [*see illustration on next page*]. These bands may be the icy equivalents of spreading centers—locations on Earth's ocean floors where tectonic plates move apart and new rock surges up. If so, the subsurface ice must have been mobile and warm at the time the features formed. But plate tectonics is a zero-sum game: if some material emerges from the interior, other material must descend. On Earth this descent occurs at subduction zones. No such zones have yet been identified on Europa.

Blame the Blobs

The mysterious mottled terrain provides further clues to Europa's interior. Galileo's images of this terrain are 10 to 100 times more detailed than Voyager's. They show it to be peppered with circular and elliptical features that the imaging team named lenticulae, Latin for "freckles." Many are domes, some are pits and some are smooth dark spots; others have a jumbled and rough texture. The dome tops look like pieces of the older ridged plains, intimating that the domes formed when the plains were pushed upward from below.

The variety of lenticulae can be explained if Europa's icy shell has behaved like a planetary lava lamp, with blobs of warm ice rising up through the colder near-surface ice. In that case, domes formed when the blobs pressed against the underside of the surface. Rough textures may be places where blobs disrupted and destroyed the plains. Smooth dark patches may be meltwater unleashed by blobs and quickly refrozen.

Blobs—technically, diapirs—would naturally develop if Europa's icy shell floated above liquid water. In this scenario, tidal flexing pumps heat into the base of the shell, where ice is near its melting temperature and most easily deformed. The warm ice is less dense than the cold ice above, so it attempts to rise. If the ice shell is thick enough, buoyancy forces can overcome the viscous resistance to flow (which lessens with depth). Like wax rising in a lava lamp, warm-ice diapirs will rise toward the surface, where they could create the visible lenticulae. Models suggest that the shell would have to be at least 10 kilometers thick.

As well as the lenticulae, mottled terrain contains the most

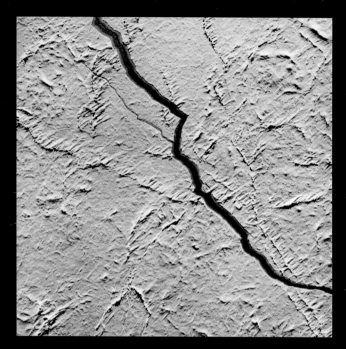

CRACKS IN THE ICE on Earth (*left*) and Europa (*right*) bear a superficial resemblance. In terrestrial polar seas, floating ice breaks apart to expose darker liquid water, which quickly freezes. The cracks can slam closed to push up ridges. On Europa, however, the dark bands and paired ridges are thought to result from tectonic processes. The scale is vastly different: this break in the sea ice is 100 meters wide, whereas the dark band on Europa is more than 15 kilometers wide.

spectacular of Europa's features: regions of "chaos." In these jumbled areas, small icy remnants of preexisting ridged plains appear to have jostled in a hummocky matrix—like icebergs calved into a slushy sea. The original arrangement of the iceberglike blocks can be reconstructed like a jigsaw puzzle, and researchers have done so for one of these areas, Conamara Chaos [*see illustration on page 41*]. If the regions formed when subsurface water melted through Europa's icy shell and then refroze, the iceberg analogy may be right on target. Another possibility is that one or more diapirs welled up and heated the near-surface ice, creating a slushy bed of ice and liquid on which the cracked and dislodged blocks of ice could slide freely. Either way, the chaos regions tell of a warm subsurface and at least partial melting.

The one type of feature the mottled terrain conspicuously lacks is small impact craters. So the surface of Europa must indeed be young. Following on Shoemaker's pioneering age estimates, researchers have modeled the solar system's comets and asteroids to understand the rate at which they impact Europa. They agree with Shoemaker's suggestion that it is primarily comets that slam into the Galilean satellites; asteroids are simply too few in number. From the presumed and observed numbers of comets in the vicinity of Jupiter—including Comet Shoemaker-Levy 9, which plunged into the gas giant in July 1994—scientists calculate that the sparsely cratered landscape of Europa is 10 million to 250 million years old. By geological standards, that is a short amount of time. Therefore, it seems likely that Europa is still active today, although no volcanic smoking guns have been found, as on Io.

The few craters that do exist on Europa's surface are themselves a probe of the thickness of the icy shell. Unlike the bowl-shaped or flat-floored impact craters on other worlds, Europa's two largest impact features have a central smooth patch surrounded by concentric rings [*see top illustration on opposite page*]. The blasts that created these features must have penetrated the rigid near-surface ice to a weak layer below. Because the weak layer was unable to maintain a crater shape, melt and slush quickly filled in, dragging the near-surface ice inward and fracturing the surface in concentric rings. In essence, the rings are the frozen record of a rock thrown into a pond—a very big rock and a very big pond. Scientists have estimated the dimensions of the original impact from the visible scars; in turn, the depth to the weak layer is six to 15 kilometers, in rough agreement with values from the tidal-heating theory and the blob models. But some regions of Europa's ice shell might be significantly thinner than others, a point researchers continue to debate.

The Bands of NIMS

In addition to its camera, the Galileo spacecraft carries a near-infrared mapping spectrometer (the NIMS instrument), which has analyzed the light reflected by Europa's surface. As expected, NIMS found the characteristic spectral bands of water ice. Yet the bands are skewed and asymmetric in shape, a sign that some impurity is mixed into the ice, especially in areas that appear dark and reddish at visible wavelengths. A prime suspect is a salt—specifically, magnesium sulfate [*see top illustration on previous page*]. If so, sitting on Europa are the biggest deposits of Epsom salt in the solar system.

Because salts are generally colorless or white, some other material must be present as well to account for the reddish color. The identity of that contaminant so far eludes scientists, but sulfur or iron compounds are suspected. Before the Galileo mission, some investigators had predicted that an internal ocean on Europa would probably be quite briny, given that many meteorites contain salts. Europa's surface materials may be revealing the chemistry of a hidden brackish ocean.

Two other Galileo instruments have also bolstered the oceanic hypothesis. The photopolarimeter-radiometer has measured temperatures across the satellite's surface. Higher latitudes are anomalously hot at night (by about five kelvins) compared with equatorial regions. This deviation could be confirmation that in addition to the weak external heating by the sun's rays, Europa has a strong internal heat source—namely, tidal flexing.

One of the most fascinating indications of Europa's present interior state has come from the Galileo magnetometer team. The Galilean satellites are immersed within the powerful magnetic field of Jupiter. Measurements of the ambient field in the vicinity of Europa show deviations associated with the satellite. These deviations might be explained if Europa has an intrinsic magnetic field, but the magnetic axis would need to be tilted at an unusually steep angle to the rotation axis. Alternatively, Europa's subsurface might be an electrical conductor, responding to the time-varying Jovian magnetic field with an induced field of its own. In this scenario the internal conductor must be as conductive as salty seawater.

Surprisingly, the magnetometer also detected a similar field near Callisto, a satellite with a heavily cratered surface that provides no hint of a subsurface ocean. An exciting possibility is that all the solar system's large icy satellites possess salty oceans within, vestiges of their warmer pasts. Galileo's final Europa flyby, planned for this coming January, will be dedicated to determining the source of the field.

Theory and observation have combined to provide a strong self-consistent case for a global ocean within Europa today. But its existence is not unequivocally proved. Warm subsurface ice could mimic many of the effects of an internal ocean. Although the satellite's surface is sparsely cratered and probably geologically young, searches for definitive evidence of ongoing geological activity have been fruitless. Europa might have had an ocean in the recent past that is now frozen solid. There is only one way to know for certain: return a spacecraft to Europa and this time go into orbit.

That is just what the National Aeronautics and Space Administration is planning to do. The Europa Orbiter mission could be launched as early as November 2003 and would enter Jupiter's orbit three years later. About two years after that, it would go into orbit around Europa at an average altitude of just 200 kilometers. Precise tracking of its position and altitude would map the gravitational field and shape of Europa in enough detail to track the ebb and flow of tides as the moon trundles around Jupiter. If Europa does have a subsurface sea, the moon's surface should rise and fall 30 meters every 3.6-day orbit; otherwise the tidal bulge will change by just one meter. In this way, the Europa Orbiter would provide the definitive test for an ocean.

Meanwhile the spacecraft's camera would photograph the satellite, and its radar would probe the subsurface for any shallow melt zones. Depending on the ice temperature and purity, the radar signal might even be able to penetrate Europa's ice shell to detect an ocean beneath, in the way Antarctica's Lake Vostok was recently mapped by radar below four kilometers of cold glacial ice [see box on next page].

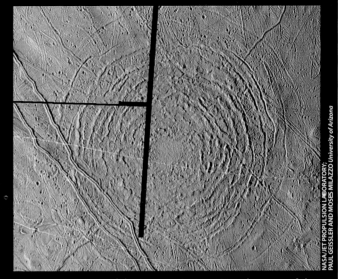

BULL'S-EYE SHAPE of the impact site Tyre Macula—one of the few large craters on Europa—hints at the presence of liquid water. The central depression is about 40 kilometers across. The surrounding rings are fractures created as the crater collapsed inward. Small secondary craters, gouged by debris from the impact, pock the surface. The black lines mark gaps in the data.

Life as we know and understand it requires three basic ingredients: energy, carbon and liquid water. Europa could have all three. Tidal flexing should heat the rocky mantle and lead to volcanism on Europa's ocean floor. At volcanic regions on Earth's ocean floors, water circulates through hot rock and emerges rich in chemical nutrients. Biological com-

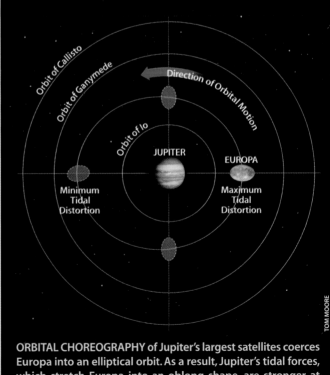

ORBITAL CHOREOGRAPHY of Jupiter's largest satellites coerces Europa into an elliptical orbit. As a result, Jupiter's tidal forces, which stretch Europa into an oblong shape, are stronger at some points in the moon's orbit than at others. (The orbits, moon, planet and tidal effects are not to scale.)

The Hidden Ocean of Europa

The Lake That Time Forgot

by Frank D. Carsey and Joan C. Horvath

If ever there were a middle of nowhere, Lake Vostok in Antarctica would be it. To get there, one would first have to go to the eponymous Russian scientific base, a place famed for its climate—widely regarded as the world's worst. Then one would have to drill four kilometers straight down. There, cut off from the outside world for the past several million years, is a body of fresh water roughly the extent of Lake Ontario and twice as deep. It may be the closest thing on Earth to the putative ocean of Europa.

The first indication of the lost lake came in the 1970s from aircraft-borne sounding radar, which can penetrate ice and reflect off the underlying rock or water. The strength of the reflected signal and the flat geometry of the under-ice surface clearly revealed water, which was confirmed by reexamination of older Russian seismic data. But researchers only fully comprehended the true size of the lake in 1996, after the smooth expanse of its icy roof had been probed by the European Remote Sensing Satellite. So far no one has drilled into it, although plans are afoot.

The top of the ice is at about 3,700 meters (12,000 feet) altitude, and the lake surface itself is just below sea level. Judging from the contours of the surrounding bedrock, the lake basin may be a tectonic rift—a ruptured area of Earth like those filled by Lake Baikal and the Red Sea. And why is water there, rather than simply more ice? Some geological evidence suggests the presence of a hot spot similar to (but smaller than) that responsible for building the Hawaiian Islands. But even without a hot spot, the trickle of heat from Earth's interior is sufficient to reach the local melting point because of the insulating effect of the ice. In fact, under-ice lakes are not uncommon in Antarctica; Vostok is simply the largest.

At about the same time Russian and British scientists were mapping Vostok, events elsewhere were revealing how precious its pristine waters could be for science. Microbes were turning up in harsh environments—around deep-sea volcanic vents, in shallower ice-covered Antarctic lakes, in alkaline lakes like California's Mono Lake—that had only one thing in common: the presence of liquid water. Meanwhile the Galileo spacecraft began finding that Europa might have its own ocean under the ice. The depth of the ice cover on Vostok and Europa is similar; except for the lower pressures on Europa (its gravity is about one seventh as strong as Earth's), conditions could be comparable. If life could colonize Lake Vostok, so the thinking goes, then maybe it could find a niche in Europa.

Three years ago we and others at the Jet Propulsion Laboratory proposed exploring both Lake Vostok and Europa using the same basic approach. Vostok would benefit from technology developed for Europa, whereas a Europan explorer could go through its paces near to home. Along with experts at the Woods Hole Oceanographic Institution and the University of Nebraska, we have investigated the possibility of a pair of devices: a "cryobot," which melts its way through the ice, and a small submarine, or "hydrobot," which searches for life and makes other measurements.

Needless to say, the design will be a challenge. The high pressures in the subsurface seas—which exceed those on the deck of the sunken *Titanic*—seem to demand a large and heavy armored hydrobot, but a large hydrobot would be difficult to send to Europa. The hydrobot must be autonomous and able to respond to a complex environment with cracks, rocks and so on. Its tiny onboard chemistry laboratories must survey the environment and search out microbes, even if they are utterly unlike those seen elsewhere. And both devices must be fully sterilized so they do not contaminate the water with commonplace microbes. Meeting all these demands is beyond the current state of the art in ice coring and miniature submersibles. But engineers are optimistic. The plan is to start exploring Lake Vostok as early as 2003 and Europa perhaps a decade later.

FRANK D. CARSEY and JOAN C. HORVATH lead the Europa/Lake Vostok Initiative at the Jet Propulsion Laboratory of the California Institute of Technology in Pasadena, Calif.

NORTH →

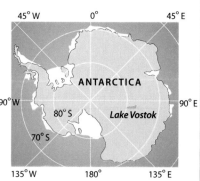

LAKE VOSTOK is tucked away in an East Antarctic rift valley and covered by about four kilometers of slowly moving ice. Above the lake, the ice floats much as an iceberg does (*left*); to support a slight rise of the ice surface, the lake surface slopes down by about 400 meters from south to north. On the bottom may be sediments. The Russian Vostok station is directly above the south end (*red dot*). (The vertical scale is distorted.)

TOM MOORE; SOURCE: FRANK D. CARSEY AND MARTIN J. SIEGERT *University of Bristol*

The Hidden Ocean of Europa

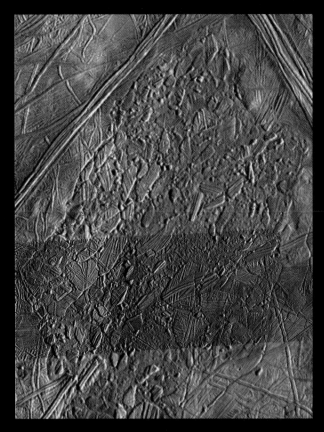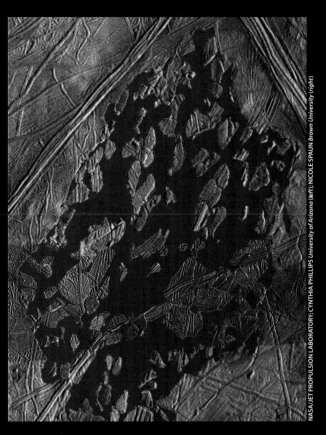

LIKE A JIGSAW PUZZLE, Conamara Chaos can be pieced back together. The Galileo spacecraft saw a jumble of ice blocks jostled and twisted within a frozen icy matrix (*left*). In their reconstruction (*right*), scientists have identified the matrix (*red*) and restored the ridge-topped ice blocks as best as possible to their original positions. But more than half of the pieces have gone missing, converted into matrix. The gnarled region testifies to the geologic vivacity of Europa.

munities thrive at these warm oases. They do, however, depend on the surface ecosystem to a large extent; most notably, oxygen dissolved in the seawater comes from photosynthesis [see "Hot Springs on the Ocean Floor," by John M. Edmond and Karen von Damm; SCIENTIFIC AMERICAN, April 1983]. Europan deep-ocean life, on the other hand, would be utterly on its own. The available chemical-energy resources would be very limited. Although microbial life might make do, biologically complex and diverse organisms of the type that inhabit Earth's oceans probably could not.

If the Europa Orbiter mission confirms the existence of a subsurface ocean, the next logical step would be to examine the surface in situ. A small robotic lander could analyze a scoopful of ice for organic compounds. Ultimately, it may be possible for a robotic submarine to melt a path through the ice shell. Europa's briny waters, now surmised only by indirect means, would then be known firsthand. It might turn out that we are not alone in the solar system after all. **SA**

The Authors

ROBERT T. PAPPALARDO, JAMES W. HEAD and RONALD GREELEY have worked together on the Galileo imaging team for several years. Pappalardo learned to appreciate Jupiter's satellites during the 1979 Voyager encounters, when he was in high school. Now a research associate at Brown University, he has also worked with various science museums to develop shows and exhibits on planetary discovery. Head began his career helping to choose Apollo landing sites and train astronauts. Since that time, he has been a geology professor at Brown and a participant in nearly every major planetary mission. He has collaborated with Russian scientists for several decades, beginning when the Iron Curtain was as much a scientific barrier as a political one. Greeley is another veteran of planetary science. He began to work for NASA while on military assignment in the pre-Apollo days. Seeing how geological principles could be applied to non-Earth objects—still a new idea at the time—he stayed on at the space agency. He is now a professor at Arizona State University.

Further Reading

GEOLOGY OF EUROPA. Baerbel K. Lucchitta and Laurence A. Soderblom in *Satellites of Jupiter.* Edited by David Morrison. University of Arizona Press, 1982.
EVIDENCE FOR A SUBSURFACE OCEAN ON EUROPA. Michael H. Carr et al. in *Nature,* Vol. 391, pages 363–365; January 22, 1998.
EUROPA: INITIAL GALILEO GEOLOGICAL OBSERVATIONS. Ronald Greeley et al. in *Icarus,* Vol. 135, pages 4–24; September 1998.
THE NEW SOLAR SYSTEM. Fourth edition. Edited by J. Kelly Beatty, Carolyn Collins Petersen and Andrew Chaikin. Cambridge University Press, 1998.
The Galileo project site is at www.jpl.nasa.gov/galileo on the World Wide Web.
The Europa Orbiter site is www.jpl.nasa.gov/ice_fire//europao. htm on the World Wide Web.

The Oort Cloud

On the outskirts of the solar system swarms a vast cloud of comets, influenced almost as much by other stars as by our sun. The dynamics of this cloud may help explain such matters as mass extinctions on Earth

by Paul R. Weissman

It is common to think of the solar system as ending at the orbit of the most distant known planet, Pluto. But the sun's gravitational influence extends more than 3,000 times farther, halfway to the nearest stars. And that space is not empty—it is filled with a giant reservoir of comets, leftover material from the formation of the solar system. That reservoir is called the Oort cloud.

The Oort cloud is the Siberia of the solar system, a vast, cold frontier filled with exiles of the sun's inner empire and only barely under the sway of the central authority. Typical noontime temperatures are a frigid four degrees Celsius above absolute zero, and neighboring comets are typically tens of millions of kilometers apart. The sun, while still the brightest star in the sky, is only about as bright as Venus in the evening sky on Earth.

We have never actually "seen" the Oort cloud. But no one has ever seen an electron, either. We infer the existence and properties of the Oort cloud and the electron from the physical effects we can observe. In the case of the former, those effects are the steady trickle of long-period comets into the planetary system. The existence of the Oort cloud answers questions that people have asked since antiquity: What are comets, and where do they come from?

Aristotle speculated in the fourth century B.C. that comets were clouds of lu-

CELESTIAL PIED PIPER, the red dwarf star Gliese 710, will crash through the Oort cloud in 1.4 million years—reanimating dormant comets, luring many out of their orbits and hurling some toward the planets. Such incursions, the result of haphazard stellar motions in our galaxy, occur every one million years on average. In this artist's conception, the distant comets are not to scale.

minous gas high in Earth's atmosphere. But the Roman philosopher Seneca suggested in the first century A.D. that they were heavenly bodies, traveling along their own paths through the firmament. Fifteen centuries passed before his hypothesis was confirmed by Danish astronomer Tycho Brahe, who compared observations of the comet of 1577 made from several different locations in Europe. If the comet had been close by, then from each location it would have had a slightly different position against the stars. Brahe could not detect any differences and concluded that the comet was farther away than the moon.

Just how much farther started to become clear only when astronomers began determining the comets' orbits. In 1705 the English astronomer Edmond Halley compiled the first catalogue of 24 comets. The observations were fairly crude, and Halley could fit only rough parabolas to each comet's path. Nevertheless, he argued that the orbits might be very long ellipses around the sun:

For so their Number will be determinate and, perhaps, not so very great. Besides, the Space between the Sun and the fix'd Stars is so immense that there is Room enough for a Comet to revolve, tho' the Period of its Revolution be vastly long.

In a sense, Halley's description of com-

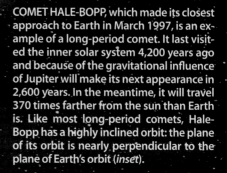

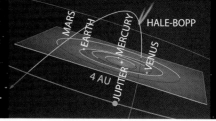

DENNIS DICICCO *Sky & Telescope*; MICHAEL GOODMAN (*inset*)

ets circulating in orbits stretching between the stars anticipated the discovery of the Oort cloud two and a half centuries later. Halley also noticed that the comets of 1531, 1607 and 1682 had very similar orbits and were spaced at roughly 76-year intervals. These seemingly different comets, he suggested, were actually the same comet returning at regular intervals. That body, now known as Halley's comet, last visited the region of the inner planets in 1986.

Since Halley's time, astronomers have divided comets into two groups according to the time it takes them to orbit the sun (which is directly related to the comets' average distance from the sun). Long-period comets, such as the recent bright comets Hyakutake and Hale-Bopp, have orbital periods greater than 200 years; short-period comets, less than 200 years. In the past decade astronomers have further divided the short-period comets into two groups: Jupiter-family comets, such as comets Encke and Tempel 2, which have periods less than 20 years; and intermediate-period, or Halley-type, comets, with periods between 20 and 200 years.

These definitions are somewhat arbitrary but reflect real differences. The intermediate- and long-period comets enter the planetary region randomly from all directions, whereas the Jupiter-family comets have orbits whose planes are typically inclined no more than 40 degrees from the ecliptic plane, the plane of Earth's orbit. (The orbits of the other planets are also very close to the ecliptic plane.) The intermediate- and long-period comets appear to come from the Oort cloud, whereas the Jupiter-family comets are now thought to originate in the Kuiper belt, a region in the ecliptic beyond the orbit of Neptune [see "The Kuiper Belt," by Jane X. Luu and David C. Jewitt; SCIENTIFIC AMERICAN, May 1996].

The Netherworld beyond Pluto

By the early 20th century, enough long-period cometary orbits were available to study their statistical distribution [*see illustration on page 47*]. A problem emerged. About one third of all the "osculating" orbits—that is, the orbits the comets were following at the point of their closest approach to the sun—were hyperbolic. Hyperbolic orbits would originate in and return to interstellar space, as opposed to elliptical orbits, which are bound by gravity to the sun. The hyperbolic orbits led some astronomers to suggest that comets were captured from interstellar space by encounters with the planets.

To examine this hypothesis, celestial-mechanics researchers extrapolated, or "integrated," the orbits of the long-period comets backward in time. They found that because of distant gravitational tugs from the planets, the osculating orbits did not represent the comets' original orbits [*see bottom illustration on opposite page*]. When the effects of the planets were accounted for—by integrating far enough back in time and orienting the orbits not in relation to the sun but in relation to the center of mass of the solar system (the sum of the sun and all the planets)—almost all the orbits became elliptical. Thus, the comets were members of the solar system, rather than interstellar vagabonds.

In addition, although two thirds of these orbits still appeared to be uniformly distributed, fully one third had orbital energies that fell within a narrow spike. That spike represented orbits that extend to very large distances—20,000 astronomical units (20,000 times the distance of Earth from the sun) or more. Such orbits have periods exceeding one million years.

Why were so many comets coming from so far away? In the late 1940s Dutch astronomer Adrianus F. van Woerkom showed that the uniform distribution could be explained by planetary perturbations, which scatter comets randomly to both larger and smaller orbits. But what about the spike of comets with million-year periods?

In 1950 Dutch astronomer Jan H. Oort, already famous for having determined the rotation of the Milky Way galaxy in the 1920s, became interested in the problem. He recognized that the million-year spike must represent the source of the long-period comets: a vast spherical cloud surrounding the planetary system and extending halfway to the nearest stars.

Oort showed that the comets in this cloud are so weakly bound to the sun that random passing stars can readily change their orbits. About a dozen stars pass within one parsec (206,000 astronomical units) of the sun every one million years. These close encounters are enough to stir the cometary orbits, randomizing their inclinations and sending

The Oort Cloud

a steady trickle of comets into the inner solar system on very long elliptical orbits [*see illustrations on next page*]. As they enter the planetary system for the first time, the comets are scattered by the planets, gaining or losing orbital energy. Some escape the solar system altogether. The remainder return and are observed again as members of the uniform distribution. Oort described the cloud as "a garden, gently raked by stellar perturbations."

A few comets still appeared to come from interstellar space. But this was probably an incorrect impression given by small errors in the determination of their orbits. Moreover, comets can shift their orbits because jets of gas and dust from their icy surfaces act like small rocket engines as the comets approach the sun. Such nongravitational forces can make the orbits appear hyperbolic when they are actually elliptical.

Shaken, Not Stirred

Oort's accomplishment in correctly interpreting the orbital distribution of the long-period comets is even more impressive when one considers that he had only 19 well-measured orbits to work with. Today astronomers

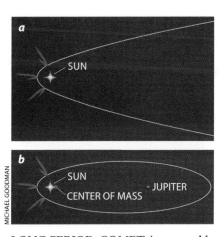

LONG-PERIOD COMET is so weakly bound to the sun that the planets have a decisive influence on it. Astronomers can usually see the comet only while it swings by the sun. When they apply Kepler's laws of celestial motion to plot its course—its "osculating," or apparent, orbit—the comet often seems to be on a hyperbolic trajectory, implying that it came from interstellar space and will return there (*a*). A more sophisticated calculation, which accounts for the planets (especially the most massive planet, Jupiter), finds that the orbit is actually elliptical (*b*). The orbit changes shape on each pass through the inner solar system.

have more than 15 times as many. They now know that long-period comets entering the planetary region for the first time come from an average distance of 44,000 astronomical units. Such orbits have periods of 3.3 million years.

Astronomers have also realized that stellar perturbations are not always gentle. Occasionally a star comes so close to the sun that it passes right through the Oort cloud, violently disrupting the cometary orbits along its path. Statistically a star is expected to pass within 10,000 astronomical units of the sun every 36 million years and within 3,000 astronomical units every 400 million years. Comets close to the star's path are thrown out to interstellar space, while the orbits of comets throughout the cloud undergo substantial changes.

Although close stellar encounters have no direct effect on the planets—the closest expected approach of any star over the history of the solar system is 900 astronomical units from the sun—they might have devastating indirect consequences. In 1981 Jack G. Hills, now at Los Alamos National Laboratory, suggested that a close stellar passage could send a "shower" of comets toward the planets, raising the rate of cometary impacts on the planets and possibly even causing a biological mass extinction on Earth. According to computer simulations I performed in 1985 with Piet Hut, then at the Institute for Advanced Study in Princeton, N.J., the frequency of comet passages during a shower could reach 300 times the normal rate. The shower would last two to three million years.

Recently Kenneth A. Farley and his colleagues at the California Institute of Technology found evidence for just such a comet shower. Using the rare helium 3 isotope as a marker for extraterrestrial material, they plotted the accumulation of interplanetary dust particles in ocean sediments over time. The rate of dust accumulation is thought to reflect the number of comets passing through the planetary region; each comet sheds dust along its path. Farley discovered that this rate increased sharply at the end of the Eocene epoch, about 36 million years ago, and decreased slowly

TIDAL FORCES arise because gravity becomes weaker with distance. Therefore, the central bulge of our galaxy—a concentration of stars at the hub of the spiral pattern—pulls more on the near side of the Oort cloud (*not to scale*) than on the far side. The galactic plane exerts a similar force in a different direction. The galactic tides are analogous to lunar tides, which arise because the side of Earth closest to the moon feels a stronger gravitational pull than the antipode does.

over two to three million years, just as theoretical models of comet showers would predict. The late Eocene is identified with a moderate biological extinction event, and several impact craters have been dated to this time. Geologists have also found other traces of impacts in terrestrial sediments, such as iridium layers and microtektites.

Is Earth in danger of a comet shower now? Fortunately not. Joan Garcia-Sanchez of the University of Barcelona, Robert A. Preston and Dayton L. Jones of the Jet Propulsion Laboratory in Pasadena, Calif., and I have been using the positions and velocities of stars, measured by the Hipparcos satellite, to reconstruct the trajectories of stars near the solar system. We have found evidence that a star has passed close to the sun in the past one million years. The next close passage of a star will occur in 1.4 million years, and that is a small red dwarf called Gliese 710, which will pass through the outer Oort cloud about 70,000 astronomical units from the sun. At that distance, Gliese 710 might increase the frequency of comet passages through the inner solar system by 50 percent—a sprinkle perhaps, but certainly no shower.

In addition to random passing stars, the Oort cloud is now known to be disturbed by two other effects. First, the cloud is sufficiently large that it feels tidal forces generated by the disk of the Milky Way and, to a lesser extent, the galactic core. These tides arise because the sun and a comet in the cloud are at slightly different distances from the midplane of the disk or from the galactic center and thus feel a slightly different gravitational tug [*see top illustration on preceding page*]. The tides help to feed new long-period comets into the planetary region.

Second, giant molecular clouds in the galaxy can perturb the Oort cloud, as Ludwig Biermann of the Max Planck Institute for Physics and Astrophysics in Munich suggested in 1978. These massive clouds of cold hydrogen, the birthplaces of stars and planetary systems, are 100,000 to one million times as massive as the sun. When the solar system comes close to one, the gravitational perturbations rip comets from their orbits and fling them into interstellar space. These encounters, though violent, are infrequent—only once every 300 million to 500 million years. In 1985 Hut and Scott D. Tremaine, now at Princeton University, showed that over the history of the solar system, molecular clouds have had about the same cumulative effect as all passing stars.

Inner Core

Currently three main questions concern Oort-cloud researchers. First, what is the cloud's structure? In 1987 Tremaine, Martin J. Duncan, now at Queen's University in Ontario, and Thomas R. Quinn, now at the University of Washington, studied how stellar and molecular-cloud perturbations redistribute comets within the Oort cloud. Comets at its outer edge are rapidly lost, either to interstellar space or to the inner solar system, because of the perturbations. But deeper inside, there probably exists a relatively dense core that slowly replenishes the outer reaches.

Tremaine, Duncan and Quinn also showed that as comets fall in from the Oort cloud, their orbital inclinations tend not to change. This is a major reason why astronomers now think the Kuiper belt, rather than the Oort cloud, accounts for the low-inclination, Jupiter-family comets. Still, the Oort cloud is the most likely source of the higher-inclination, intermediate-period comets, such as Halley and Swift-Tuttle. They were probably once long-period comets that the planets pulled into shorter-period orbits.

The second main question is, How many comets inhabit the Oort cloud? The number depends on how fast comets leak from the cloud into interplanetary space.

To account for the observed number of long-period comets, astronomers now estimate the cloud has six trillion comets, making Oort-cloud comets the most abundant substantial bodies in the solar system. Only a sixth of them are in the outer, dynamically active cloud first described by Oort; the remainder are in the relatively dense core. If the best estimate for the average mass of a comet—about 40 billion metric tons—is applied, the total mass of comets in the Oort cloud at present is about 40 times that of Earth.

Finally, from where did the Oort-cloud comets originally come? They could not have formed at their current position, because material at those distances is too sparse to coalesce. Nor could they have originated in interstellar space; capture of comets by the sun is very inefficient. The only place left is the planetary system. Oort speculated that the comets were created in the asteroid belt and ejected by the giant planets during the formation of the solar system. But comets are icy bodies, essentially big, dirty snowballs, and the asteroid belt was too warm for ices to condense.

A year after Oort's 1950 paper, astronomer Gerard P. Kuiper of the University of Chicago proposed that comets coalesced farther from the sun, among the giant planets. (The Kuiper belt is named for him because he suggested that some comets also formed beyond the farthest planetary orbits.) Comets probably originated throughout the giant planets' region, but researchers used to argue that those near Jupiter and Saturn, the two most massive planets, would have been ejected to interstellar space rather than to the Oort cloud. Uranus and Neptune, with their lower masses, could not easily throw so many comets onto escape trajectories. But more recent dynamical studies have cast some doubt on this scenario. Jupiter and particularly Saturn do place a significant fraction of their comets into the Oort cloud. Although this fraction may be smaller than that of Uranus and Neptune, it may have been offset by the greater amount of material initially in the larger planets' zones.

Therefore, the Oort-cloud comets may have come from a wide range of solar distances and hence a wide range of formation temperatures. This fact may help explain some of the compositional diversity observed in comets. Indeed, recent work I have done with

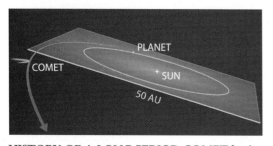

HISTORY OF A LONG-PERIOD COMET begins when it forms near the planets and is catapulted by them into a wide orbit.

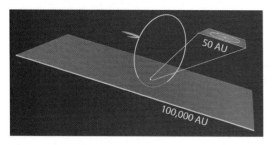

There the comet is susceptible to the gravitational forces of random passing stars and giant molecular clouds, as well as the tidal forces of the galactic disk and core. These forces randomly tilt the orbital plane of the comet and gradually pull it farther out.

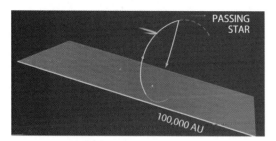

Beyond a distance of about 20,000 astronomical units (20,000 times the Earth-sun distance), the various outside influences are capable of throwing the comet back toward the planets.

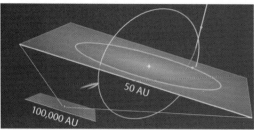

Once the comet reenters the inner solar system, the planets may pull it to a new orbit, so that it reappears on a regular basis.

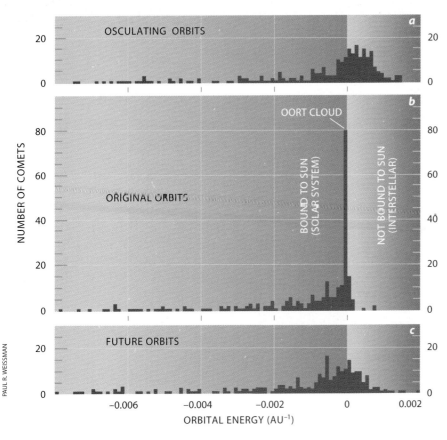

PAUL R. WEISSMAN

ORBITAL ENERGY of known long-period comets, as shown in these histograms, reveals the Oort cloud. Astronomers first calculate the osculating orbits of the comets—the orbits they would take if their motion were entirely caused by the sun's gravity. One third of these orbits have a positive energy, making them appear interstellar (*a*). But when corrected for the influence of the planets and extrapolated backward in time, the energy is slightly negative—indicating that the comets came from the edge of the solar system (*b*). A few comets still seem to be interstellar, but this is probably the result of small observational errors. As the planets continue to exert their influence, some comets will return to the Oort cloud, some will escape from the solar system and the rest will revisit the inner solar system (*c*). Technically, the orbital energy is proportional to the reciprocal of the semimajor axis, expressed in units of inverse astronomical units (AU^{-1}).

Harold F. Levison of the Southwest Research Institute in Boulder, Colo., has shown that the cloud may even contain asteroids from the inner planets' region. These objects, made of rock rather than ice, may constitute 2 to 3 percent of the total Oort-cloud population.

The key to these ideas is the presence of the giant planets, which hurl the comets outward and modify their orbits if they ever reenter the planetary region. If other stars have giant planets, as observations over the past few years suggest, they may have Oort clouds, too. If each star has its own cloud, then as stars pass by the sun, their Oort clouds will pass through our cloud. Even so, collisions between comets will be rare because the typical space between comets is an astronomical unit or more.

The Oort clouds around each star may slowly be leaking comets into interstellar space. These interstellar comets should be easily recognizable if they were to pass close to the sun, because they would approach the solar system at much higher velocities than the comets from our own Oort cloud. To date, no such interstellar comets have ever been detected. This fact is not surprising: because the solar system is a very small target in the vastness of interstellar space, there is at best a 50–50 chance that people should have seen one interstellar comet by now.

The Oort cloud continues to fascinate astronomers. Through the good fortunes of celestial mechanics, nature has preserved a sample of material from the formation of the solar system in this distant reservoir. By studying it and the cosmo-chemical record frozen in its icy members, researchers are learning valuable clues about the origin of the solar system.

Several space missions are now being readied to unlock those secrets. The Stardust spacecraft, due for launch next year, will fly through the coma of comet Wild 2, collect samples of cometary dust and return them to Earth for laboratory analysis. A few years later the CONTOUR probe will fly by three comets and compare their compositions. The Deep Space 4/Champollion mission will send an orbiter and a lander to comet Tempel 1, and the Rosetta mission will do the same for comet Wirtanen. The new millennium is going to be a wonderful time for studying comets. **SA**

The Author

PAUL R. WEISSMAN is a senior research scientist at the Jet Propulsion Laboratory in Pasadena, Calif., where he specializes in studies of the physics and dynamics of comets. He is also the project scientist for NASA's Deep Space 4/Champollion mission, which is scheduled to land on short-period comet Tempel 1 in 2005. Weissman has written more than 80 refereed scientific papers and is one of three editors of the *Encyclopedia of the Solar System*, to be published by Academic Press this fall.

Further Reading

COMETS: A CHRONOLOGICAL HISTORY OF OBSERVATION, SCIENCE, MYTH AND FOLKLORE. Donald K. Yeomans. John Wiley & Sons, 1991.
COMETS IN THE POST-HALLEY ERA. Edited by Ray L. Newburn, Jr., Marcia Neugebauer and Jurgen Rahe. Kluwer Academic Publishers, 1991.
DYNAMICS OF COMETS: RECENT DEVELOPMENTS AND NEW CHALLENGES. Julio A. Fernandez in *Asteroids, Comets, Meteors 1993: Proceedings of the 160th Symposium of the International Astronomical Union.* Edited by A. Milani, M. Di Martino and A. Cellino. Kluwer Academic Publishers, 1994.
COMPLETING THE INVENTORY OF THE SOLAR SYSTEM. Edited by Terrence W. Rettig and Joseph M. Hahn. Astronomical Society of the Pacific Conference Series, Vol. 107; 1996.

SOHO Reveals
the Secrets of the Sun

A powerful new spacecraft—the Solar and Heliospheric
Observatory, or SOHO—is now monitoring the sun around
the clock, providing new clues about our nearest star

by Kenneth R. Lang

From afar, the sun does not look very complex. To the casual observer, it is just a smooth, uniform ball of gas. Close inspection, however, shows that the star is in constant turmoil—a fact that fuels many fundamental mysteries. For instance, scientists do not understand how the sun generates its magnetic fields, which are responsible for most solar activity, including unpredictable explosions that cause magnetic storms and power blackouts here on Earth. Nor do they know why this magnetism is concentrated into so-called sunspots, dark islands on the sun's surface that are as large as Earth and thousands of times more magnetic. Furthermore, physicists cannot explain why the sun's magnetic activity varies dramatically, waning and intensifying again every 11 years or so.

To solve such puzzles—and better predict the sun's impact on our planet—the European Space Agency (ESA) and the National Aeronautics and Space Administration launched the two-ton Solar and Heliospheric Observatory (SOHO, for short) on December 2, 1995. The spacecraft reached its permanent strategic position—which is called the inner Lagrangian point and is about 1 percent of the way to the sun—on February 14, 1996. There SOHO is balanced between the pull of Earth's gravity and the sun's gravity and so orbits the sun together with Earth. Earlier spacecraft studying the sun orbited Earth, which would regularly obstruct their view. In contrast, SOHO monitors the sun continuously: 12 instruments examine the sun in unprecedented detail. They downlink several thousand images a day through NASA's Deep Space Network antennae to SOHO's Experimenters' Operations Facility at the NASA Goddard Space Flight Center located in Greenbelt, Md.

At the Experimenters' Operations Facility, solar physicists

from around the world work together, watching the sun night and day from a room without windows. Many of the unique images they receive move nearly instantaneously to the SOHO home page on the World Wide Web (located at http://sohowww.nascom.nasa.gov). When these pictures first began to arrive, the sun was at the very bottom of its 11-year activity cycle. But SOHO carries enough fuel to continue operating for a decade or more. Thus, it will keep watch over the sun through all its tempestuous seasons—from the recent lull in magnetic activity to its next maximum, which should take place at the end of the century. Already, though, SOHO has offered some astounding findings.

Exploring Unseen Depths

To understand the sun's cycles, we must look deep inside the star, to where its magnetism is generated. One way to explore these unseen depths is by tracing the in-and-out, heaving motions of the sun's outermost visible surface, named the photosphere from the Greek word *photos*, meaning "light." These oscillations, which can be tens of kilometers high and travel a few hundred meters per second, arise from sounds that course through the solar interior. The sounds are trapped inside the sun; they cannot propagate through the near vacuum of space. (Even if they could reach Earth, they are too low for human hearing.) Nevertheless, when these sounds strike the sun's surface and rebound back down, they disturb the gases there, causing them to rise and fall, slowly and rhythmically, with a period of about five minutes. The throbbing motions these sounds create are imperceptible to the naked eye, but SOHO instruments routinely pick them out.

The surface oscillations are the combined effect of about 10 million separate notes—each of which has a unique path of propagation and samples a well-defined section inside the sun. So to trace the star's physical landscape all the way through—from its churning convection zone, the outer 28.7 percent (by radius), into its radiative zone and core—we must determine the precise pitch of all the notes.

The dominant factor affecting each sound is its speed, which in turn depends on the temperature and composition of the solar regions through which it passes. SOHO scientists compute the expected sound speed using a numerical model. They then use relatively small discrepancies between their computer calculations and the observed sound speed to fine-tune the model and establish the sun's radial variation in temperature, density and composition.

At present, theoretical expectations and observations made with SOHO's Michelson Doppler Imager (MDI) telescope are in close agreement, showing a maximum difference of only 0.2 percent. Where these discrepancies occur is, in fact, significant. They suggest that turbulent material is moving in and out just below the convection zone and hint that such mixing motions might occur at the boundary of the energy-generating core—concepts that could be very important for studies of stellar evolution.

For more than three centuries, astronomers have known from watching sunspots that the photosphere rotates faster at

opposite page: COURTESY OF SOHO EIT CONSORTIUM (inner region) AND SOHO UVCS CONSORTIUM (outer region)

ESA AND NASA

COMPOSITE IMAGE (*left*), taken by two instruments on board SOHO (*above*) and joined at the black circle, reveals the sun's outer atmosphere from the base of the corona to millions of kilometers above the solar surface. Raylike structures appear in the ultraviolet light emitted by oxygen ions flowing away from the sun to form the solar wind (*outside black circle*). The solar wind with the highest speed originates in coronal holes, which appear as dark regions at the north pole (*top*) and across the solar disk (*inside black circle*).

SOHO Reveals the Secrets of the Sun

MAGNIFICENT COSMOS 49

the equator than at higher latitudes and that the speed decreases evenly toward each pole. SOHO data confirm that this differential pattern persists through the convection zone. Furthermore, the rotation speed becomes uniform from pole to pole about a third of the way down. Thus, the rotation velocity changes sharply at the base of the convection zone. There the outer parts of the radiative interior, which rotates at one speed, meet the overlying convection zone, which spins faster in its equatorial middle. We now suspect that this thin base layer of rotational shear may be the source of the sun's magnetism.

The MDI telescope on board SOHO has also helped probe the sun's outer shells. Because its lenses are positioned well above Earth's obscuring atmosphere, it can continuously resolve fine detail that cannot always be seen from the ground. For this reason, it has proved particularly useful in time-distance helioseismology, a new technique for revealing the motion of gases just below the photosphere. The method is quite straightforward: the telescope records small periodic changes in the wavelength of light emitted from a million points across the sun every minute. By keeping track of them, it is possible to determine how long it takes for sound waves to skim through the sun's outer layers. This travel time tells of both the temperature and gas flows along the internal path connecting two points on the visible solar surface. If the local temperature is high, sound waves move more quickly—as they do if they travel with the flow of gas.

The MDI has provided travel times for sounds crossing thousands of paths, linking myriad surface points. And SOHO scientists have used these data to chart the three-dimensional internal structure and dynamics of the sun, much in the same way that a computed tomographic (CT) scan creates an image of the inside of the brain. They fed the SOHO data to supercomputers to work out temperatures and flow directions along these intersecting paths. Using these techniques during two years of nearly continuous observations, SOHO scientists have discovered vast rivers of hot gas that circulate within the sun.

Completely unexpected currents circle the polar regions of the sun just below the photosphere. They seem to resemble the jet streams high in the atmosphere of Earth, which have a major influence on terrestrial weather. Ringing the sun at about 75 degrees latitude, the solar jet streams are totally inside the sun, 40,000 kilometers (25,000 miles) below the photosphere, and cannot be seen at the visible surface. They move about 10 percent faster than the surrounding gas—about 130 kilometers per hour faster—and they are wide enough to engulf two planet Earths.

The outer layer of the sun, to a depth of at least 25,000 kilometers, is also slowly flowing from the equator to the poles, at a speed of about 90 kilometers per hour. At this rate, an object would be transported from the equator to the pole in little more than a year. Of course, the sun rotates at a much faster rate of about 7,000 kilometers per hour, completing one revolution at the equator in 25.7 days. The combination of differential rotation and poleward flow has been the explanation for the stretched-out shapes of magnetic regions that have migrated toward the poles. The new SOHO MDI observations demonstrate for the first time that the poleward flow reaches deeply into the sun, penetrating at least 12 percent of the convection zone.

Researchers have also identified internal rivers of gas mov-

COURTESY OF JACK HARVEY *National Optical Astronomy Observatories*; CROSS SECTIONS BY MICHAEL GOODMAN

SOUND WAVES,
represented here by black lines inside the cutaway section, resonate throughout the sun. They are produced by hot gas churning in the convection zone, which lies above the radiative zone and the sun's core. As sound waves travel toward the sun's center, they gain speed and are refracted back out. At the same time, the sun's surface reflects waves traveling outward back in. Thus, the entire star throbs, with regions pulsing in (*red spots*) and out (*blue spots*).

CONVECTION ZONE

RADIATIVE ZONE

ENERGY-GENERATING CORE

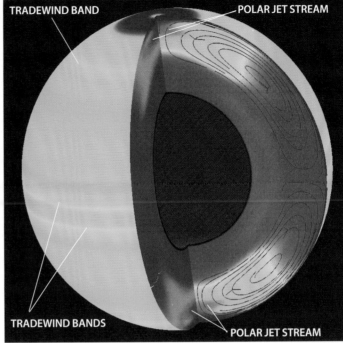

ing in bands near the equator at different speeds relative to each other in both the northern and southern hemispheres. The solar belts are more than 64,000 kilometers in width and move about 16 kilometers per hour faster than the gases to either side. These broad belts of higher-velocity currents remind one of Earth's equatorial tradewinds and also of Jupiter's colorful, banded atmosphere. The bands are deeply rooted, extending down approximately 19,000 kilometers into the sun. The full extent of the newfound solar meteorology could never have been seen by looking at the visible layer of the solar atmosphere.

The MDI team also investigated horizontal motions at a depth of about 1,400 kilometers and compared them with an overlying magnetic image, also taken by the MDI instrument. They found that strong magnetic concentrations tend to lie in regions where the subsurface gas flow converges. Thus, the churning gas probably forces magnetic fields together and concentrates them, thereby overcoming the outward magnetic pressure that ought to make such localized concentrations expand and disperse.

The Million-Degree Corona

SOHO is also helping scientists explain the solar atmosphere, or corona. The sun's sharp outer rim is illusory. It merely marks the level beyond which solar gas becomes transparent. The invisible corona extends beyond the planets and presents one of the most puzzling paradoxes of solar physics: it is unexpectedly hot, reaching temperatures of more than one million kelvins just above the photosphere; the sun's visible surface is only 5,780 kelvins. Heat simply should not flow outward from a cooler to a hotter region. It violates the second law of thermodynamics and all common sense as well. Thus, there must be some mechanism transporting energy from the photosphere, or below, out to the corona. Both kinetic and magnetic energy can flow from cold to hot regions. So writhing gases and shifting magnetic fields may be accountable.

For studying the corona and identifying its elusive heating mechanism, physicists look at ultraviolet (UV), extreme ultraviolet (EUV) and x-ray radiation. This is because hot material—such as that within the corona—emits most of its energy at these wavelengths. Also, the photosphere is too cool to emit intense radiation at these wavelengths, so it appears dark under the hot gas. Unfortunately, UV, EUV and x-rays are partially or totally absorbed by Earth's atmosphere, and so they must be observed through telescopes in space. SOHO is now measuring radiation at UV and EUV wavelengths using four instruments: the Extreme-ultraviolet Imaging Telescope (EIT), the Solar Ultraviolet Measurements of Emitted Radiation

(SUMER), the Coronal Diagnostic Spectrometer (CDS) and the UltraViolet Coronagraph Spectrometer (UVCS).

To map out structures across the solar disk, ranging in temperature from 6,000 to two million kelvins, SOHO makes use of spectral lines. These lines appear when the sun's radiation intensity is displayed as a function of wavelength. The various SOHO instruments locate regions having a specific temperature by tuning into spectral lines emitted by the ions formed there. Atoms in a hotter gas lose more electrons through collisions, and so they become more highly ionized. Because these different ions emit spectral lines at different wavelengths, they serve as a kind of thermometer. We can also infer the speed of the material moving in these regions from the Doppler wavelength changes of the spectral lines that SOHO records.

Ultraviolet radiation has recently revealed that the sun is a vigorous, violent place even when its 11-year activity cycle is in an apparent slump—and this fact may help explain why the corona is so hot. The whole sun seems to sparkle in the UV light emitted by localized bright spots. According to SOHO measurements, these ubiquitous hot spots are formed at a temperature of a million kelvins, and they seem to originate in small, magnetic loops of hot gas found all over the sun, including both its north and south poles. Some of these spots explode and hurl material outward at speeds of hundreds of kilometers per second. SOHO scientists are now studying these bright spots to see if they play an important role in the elusive coronal heating mechanism.

SOHO has provided direct evidence for the transfer of magnetic energy from the sun's visible surface toward the corona above. Images of the photosphere's magnetism, taken with SOHO's MDI, reveal ubiquitous pairs of opposite magnetic polarity, each joined by a magnetic arch that rises above them, like bridges that connect two magnetic islands. Energy flows from these magnetic loops when they interact, producing electrical and magnetic "short circuits." The very strong electric currents in these short circuits can heat the corona to a temperature of several million degrees. Images from the EIT

STANFORD-LOCKHEED INSTITUTE FOR SPACE RESEARCH AND NASA GODDARD SPACE FLIGHT CENTER

MAGNETIC CARPET is formed by the complex distribution and mixing of magnetic polarities (*black and white dots*). Magnetic loops, connecting regions of opposing magnetic polarity, rise far into the solar corona. The bright active regions, anchored in magnetically intense sunspots, have long been known to be sources of heating; the diffuse coronal heating appears to be associated with the ubiquitous magnetic carpet.

and CDS instruments on SOHO show the hot gases of the ever-changing corona reacting to the evolving magnetic fields rooted in the solar surface.

To explore changes at higher levels in the sun's atmosphere, SOHO relies on its UVCS and its Large Angle Spectroscopic COronagraph (LASCO). Both instruments use occulting disks to block the photosphere's underlying glare. LASCO detects visible sunlight scattered by electrons in the corona. Initially it revealed a simple corona—one that was highly symmetrical and stable. This corona, viewed during the sun's magnetic lull, exhibited pronounced holes in the north and south. (Coronal holes are extended, low-density, low-temperature regions where EUV and x-ray emissions are abnormally low or absent.)

In contrast, the equatorial regions were ringed by straight, flat streamers of outflowing matter. The sun's magnetic field shapes these streamers. At their base, electrified matter is densely concentrated within magnetized loops rooted in the photosphere. Farther out in the corona, the streamers narrow into long stalks that stretch tens of millions of kilometers into space. These extensions confine material at temperatures of about two million kelvins within their elongated magnetic boundaries, creating a belt of hot gas that extends around the sun.

The streamers live up to their name: material seems to flow continuously along their open magnetic fields. Occasionally the coronagraphs record dense concentrations of material moving through an otherwise unchanging streamer—like seeing leaves floating on a moving stream. And sometimes tremendous eruptions, called coronal mass ejections, punctuate the

CORONAL MASS EJECTIONS (*white*), occurring on the east and west sides of the sun, were recorded within hours on the same day by one of SOHO's coronagraphs. The black occulting disk blocks the glare of the sun, whose visible edge is represented here by the white circle.

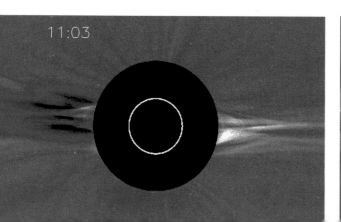

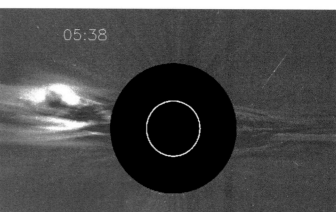

COURTESY OF SOHO LASCO CONSORTIUM AND GUENTER E. BRUECKNER

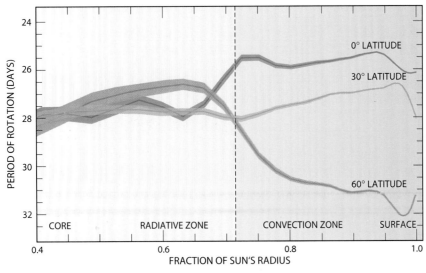

INTERNAL ROTATION RATE OF THE SUN at latitudes of zero, 30 and 60 degrees has been inferred using data from the Michelson Doppler Imager. Down to the base of the convection zone, the polar regions spin more slowly than the equatorial ones do. Beyond that, uniform rotation appears to be the norm, although scientists have not yet determined rotation rates within the sun's core.

steady outward flow. These ejections hurl billions of tons of million-degree gases into interplanetary space at speeds of hundreds of kilometers per second. This material often reaches Earth in only two or three days. To almost everyone's astonishment, LASCO found equatorial ejections emitted within hours of each other from opposite sides of the sun.

The coronagraphs have only a side view of the sun and so can barely see material moving to or from Earth. But based on what we can see, we guess that these ejections are global disturbances, extending all the way around the sun. In fact, unexpectedly wide regions of the sun seem to convulse when the star releases coronal mass ejections, at least during the minimum in the 11-year activity cycle. And the coronagraphs have detected that a few days before the ejections, the streamer belt gets brighter, suggesting that more material is accruing there. The pressure and tension of this added material probably build until the streamer belt blows open in the form of an ejection. The entire process is most likely related to a large-scale global reorganization of the sun's magnetic field.

Solar Winds and Beyond

The sun's hot and stormy atmosphere is forever expanding in all directions, filling the solar system with a ceaseless flow—called the solar wind—that contains electrons, ions and magnetic fields. The million-degree corona creates an outward pressure that overcomes the sun's gravitational attraction, enabling this perpetual outward flow. The wind accelerates as it moves away from the sun, like water overflowing a dam. As the corona disperses, it must be replaced by gases welling up from below to feed the wind. Earlier spacecraft measurements, as well as those from Ulysses (launched in 1990), showed that the wind has a fast and a slow component. The fast one moves at about 800 kilometers per second; the slow one travels at half that speed.

The slow component is associated with equatorial regions of the sun, now being scrutinized by LASCO and UVCS. These instruments suggest that the slow component of the solar wind flows out along the stalklike axes of equatorial coronal streamers. The high-speed component pours forth from the polar coronal holes. (Open magnetic fields there allow charged particles to escape the sun's gravitational and magnetic grasp.) SOHO is now investigating whether polar plumes—tall structures rooted in the photosphere that extend into the

coronal holes—help to generate this high-speed solar wind.

SOHO's UVCS has examined the spectral emission of hydrogen and heavily charged oxygen ions in the regions where the corona is heated and the solar wind accelerates. And these spectral-line profiles have produced surprising results, revealing a marked difference in the agitation speeds at which hydrogen and oxygen ions move. In polar coronal holes, where the fast solar wind originates, the heavier oxygen is far more agitated, with about 60 times more energy of motion; above two solar radii from the sun's center, oxygen has the higher agitation speed, approaching 500 kilometers per second. Hydrogen, on the other hand, moves at only 250 kilometers per second. In contrast, within equatorial regions, where the slow-speed wind begins, the lighter hydrogen moves faster than the oxygen, as one would expect from a heat-driven wind.

Researchers are now trying to determine why the more massive oxygen ions move at greater speeds in coronal holes. One possibility is that the ions are whirling around magnetic-field lines that stretch from the sun. Information about the heating and acceleration processes is probably retained within the low-density coronal holes, wherein ions rarely collide with electrons. Frequent collisions in high-density streamers might erase any signature of the relevant processes.

SOHO has obtained marvelous results to date. It has revealed features on the mysterious sun never seen before or never seen so clearly. It has provided new insights into fundamental unsolved problems, all the way from the sun's interior to Earth and out to the farthest reaches of the solar wind. Some of its instruments are now poised to resolve several other mysteries. Two of them will soon have looked at the solar oscillations long enough, and deep enough, to determine the temperature and rotation at the sun's center. Moreover, during the next few years, our home star's inner turmoil and related magnetic activity—which can directly affect our daily lives—will increase. SOHO should then offer even greater scientific returns, determining how its threatening eruptions and hot, gusty winds originate and perhaps predicting conditions in the sun's atmosphere. **SA**

The Author

KENNETH R. LANG is professor of astronomy at Tufts University. His recent illustrated book, *Sun, Earth and Sky*, describes all aspects of the sun and its interactions with Earth. Lang has also written more than 150 professional articles and four additional books, which have been translated into seven languages. Among them is the classic reference *Astrophysical Formulae*. This article updates a version that appeared in *Scientific American* in March 1997.

Detecting Massive Neutrinos

*A giant detector in the heart of Mount Ikenoyama in Japan
has demonstrated that the neutrino metamorphoses in flight,
strongly suggesting that these ghostly particles have mass*

by Edward Kearns, Takaaki Kajita and Yoji Totsuka

One man's trash is another man's treasure. For a physicist, the trash is "background"—some unwanted reaction, probably from a mundane and well-understood process. The treasure is "signal"—a reaction that we hope reveals new knowledge about the way the universe works. Case in point: over the past two decades, several groups have been hunting for the radioactive decay of the proton, an exceedingly rare signal (if it occurs at all) buried in a background of reactions caused by elusive particles called neutrinos. The proton, one of the main constituents of atoms, seems to be immortal. Its decay would be a strong indication of processes described by Grand Unified Theories that many believe lie beyond the extremely successful Standard Model of particle physics. Huge proton-decay detectors were placed deep underground, in mines or tunnels around the world, to escape the constant rain of particles called cosmic rays. But no matter how deep they went, these devices were still exposed to penetrating neutrinos produced by the cosmic rays.

The first generation of proton-decay detectors, operating from 1980 to 1995, saw no signal, no signs of proton decay—but along the way the researchers found that the supposedly mundane neutrino background was not so easy to understand. One such experiment, Kamiokande, was located in Kamioka, Japan, a mining town about 250 kilometers (155 miles) from Tokyo (as the neutrino

SUPER-KAMIOKANDE DETECTOR resides in an active zinc mine inside Mount Ikenoyama. Its stainless-steel tank contains 50,000 tons of ultrapure water, so transparent that light can pass through nearly 70 meters before losing half its intensity (for a typical swimming pool the figure is a few meters). The water is monitored by 11,000 photomultiplier tubes that cover the walls, floor and ceiling. Each tube is a hand-blown, evacuated glass bulb half a meter in diameter, coated on the inside with a thin layer of alkali metal. The photomultiplier tubes register conical flashes of Cherenkov light, which signal each rare collision of a high-energy neutrino with an atomic nucleus in the water. Technicians in inflatable rafts clean the bulbs while the tank is being filled (*inset*).

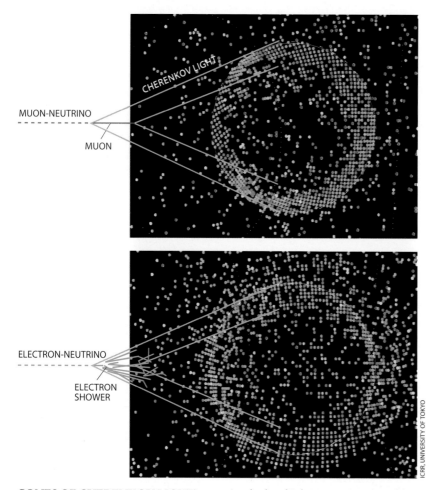

CONES OF CHERENKOV LIGHT are emitted when high-energy neutrinos hit a nucleus and produce a charged particle. A muon-neutrino (*top*) creates a muon, which travels perhaps one meter and projects a sharp ring of light onto the detectors. An electron, produced by an electron-neutrino (*bottom*), generates a small shower of electrons and positrons, each with its own Cherenkov cone, resulting in a fuzzy ring of light. Green dots indicate light detected in the same narrow time interval.

likely have mass. And in that case, these ethereal particles could collectively outweigh all the stars in the universe.

Building a Bigger Neutrino Trap

As is so often the case in particle physics, the way to make progress is to build a bigger machine. Super-Kamiokande, or Super-K for short, took the basic design of Kamiokande and scaled it up by about a factor of 10 [*see illustration on page 54*]. An array of light-sensitive detectors looks in toward the center of 50,000 tons of water whose protons may decay or get struck by a neutrino. In either case, the reaction creates particles that are spotted by means of a flash of blue light known as Cherenkov light, an optical analogue of a sonic boom, discovered by Pavel A. Cherenkov in 1934. Much as an aircraft flying faster than the speed of sound produces a shock wave of sound, an electrically charged particle (such as an electron or muon) emits Cherenkov light when it exceeds the speed of light in the medium in which it is moving. This motion does not violate Einstein's theory of relativity, for which the crucial velocity is c, the speed of light in a vacuum. In water, light propagates 25 percent slower than c, but other highly energetic particles can still travel almost as fast as c itself. Cherenkov light is emitted in a cone along the flight path of such particles.

In Super-K, the charged particle generally travels just a few meters and the Cherenkov cone projects a ring of light onto the wall of photon detectors [*see illustration on this page*]. The size, shape and intensity of this ring reveal the properties of the charged particle, which in turn tell us about the neutrino that produced it. We can easily distinguish the Cherenkov patterns of electrons from those of muons: the electrons generate a shower of particles, leading to a fuzzy ring quite unlike the crisper circle from a muon. From the Cherenkov light we also measure the energy and direction of the electron or muon, which are decent approximations to those of the neutrino.

Super-K cannot easily identify the third type of neutrino, the tau-neutrino. Such a neutrino can only interact with a nucleus and make a tau particle if it has enough energy. A muon is about 200 times as heavy as an electron; the tau about 3,500 times. The muon mass is well within the range of atmospheric neutrinos, but only a tiny fraction are at tau energies, so

flies). The name stood for "Kamioka Nucleon Decay Experiment." Scientists there and at the IMB experiment, located in a salt mine near Cleveland, Ohio, used sensitive detectors to peer into ultrapure water, waiting for the telltale flash of a proton decaying.

Such an event would have been hidden, like a needle in a small haystack, among about 1,000 similar flashes caused by neutrinos interacting with the water's atomic nuclei. Although no proton decay was seen, the analysis of those 1,000 reactions uncovered a real treasure—tantalizing evidence that the neutrinos were unexpectedly fickle, changing from one species to another in midflight. If true, that phenomenon was just as exciting and theory-bending as proton decay.

Neutrinos are amazing, ghostly particles. Every second, 60 billion of them, mostly from the sun, pass through each square centimeter of your body (and of everything else). But because they seldom interact with other particles, generally all 60 billion go through you without so much as nudging a single atom. In fact, you could send a beam of such neutrinos through a light-year of lead, and most of them would emerge totally unscathed at the far end. A detector as large as Kamiokande catches only a tiny fraction of the neutrinos that pass through it every year.

Neutrinos come in three flavors, corresponding to their three charged partners in the Standard Model: the electron and its heavier relatives, the muon and the tau particle. An electron-neutrino interacting with an atomic nucleus can produce an electron; a muon-neutrino makes a muon; a tau-neutrino, a tau. For most of the seven decades since neutrinos were first posited, physicists have assumed that they are massless. But if they can change from one flavor to another, quantum theory indicates that they most

Mapping the Universe

by Stephen D. Landy

E ven for most astronomers, a galaxy is a sizable thing—a throng of hundreds of billions of stars, threaded with gargantuan clouds of gas and dust, in a region hundreds of thousands of light-years across. But for cosmologists, those who study nature on its very largest scales, a galaxy is merely the basic unit of matter. Billions of them fill the observable universe. They congregate into clusters three million or more light-years across, which in turn constitute progressively larger assemblages. On all scales observed thus far by astronomers, galaxies appear to cluster and form intricate structures—presumably through physical processes that were dominant during the early expansion of the universe and later through gravitational interactions.

Yet there is a paradox. The clumpiness of galaxies runs contrary to one of the essential tenets of modern cosmology: the cosmological principle, the concept that the universe overall is homogeneous and isotropic, that it has no preferred place or orientation. Whenever cosmologists discuss the global properties of the universe, such as its mean density, expansion rate and shape, they do so under the auspices of this principle. On some large scale, such as that of the whole observable cosmos with a radius of 15 billion light-years, the distribution of these galactic motes should approach uniformity. But how can the evenness of matter on the ultimate scale be reconciled with the unevenness of matter on smaller scales?

Over the past several years, technological advances have enabled astronomers and cosmologists to probe the arrangement of galaxies at great distances. The naive notion that at some scale the cosmos becomes uniform has been replaced by an appreciation that the large-scale structure of the universe must be understood in terms of random processes. Although the universe is still considered to be homogeneous and isotropic, this is true only in a subtle, statistical sense. These insights are helping untangle some of the thorniest issues in cosmology:

Another implication is that the neutrino mass should now be considered in the bookkeeping of the mass of the universe. For some time, astronomers have been trying to tabulate how much mass is found in luminous matter, such as stars, and in ordinary matter that is difficult to see, such as brown dwarfs or diffuse gas. The total mass can also be measured indirectly from the orbital motion of galaxies and the rate of expansion of the universe. The direct accounting falls short of these indirect measures by about a factor of 20. The neutrino mass suggested by our result is too small to resolve this mystery by itself. Nevertheless, neutrinos created during the big bang permeate space and could account for a mass nearly equal to the combined mass of all the stars. They could have affected the formation of large astronomical structures, such as galaxy clusters.

Finally, our data have an immediate implication for two experiments that are soon to commence. Based on the earlier hints from smaller detectors, many physicists have decided to stop relying on the free but uncontrollable neutrinos from cosmic rays and instead are creating them with high-energy accelerators. Even so, the neutrinos must travel a long distance for the oscillation effect to be observed. So the neutrino beams are aimed at a detector hundreds of kilometers away. One such detector is being built in a mine in Soudan, Minn., optimized to study neutrinos sent from the Fermilab accelerator near Batavia, Ill., 730 kilometers away on the outskirts of Chicago.

Of course, a good atmospheric neutrino detector is also a good accelerator neutrino detector, so in Japan we are using Super-K to monitor a beam of neutrinos created at the KEK accelerator laboratory 250 kilometers away. Unlike atmospheric neutrinos, the beam can be turned on and off and has

a well-defined energy and direction. Most important, we have placed a detector similar to Super-K near the origin of the beam to characterize the muon-neutrinos before they oscillate. Effectively, we are using the ratio (again) of the counts near the source to those far away to cancel uncertainty and verify

the effect. As this article is being printed, neutrinos in the first long-distance artificial neutrino beam are passing under the mountains of Japan, with 50,000 tons of Super-K capturing a small handful. Exactly how many it captures will be the next chapter in this story.

Other Puzzles, Other Possibilities

There are other indications of neutrino mass that particle physicists are trying to sort out. For more than 30 years, scientists have been capturing some of the electron-neutrinos that are generated by nuclear fusion processes in the sun. These experiments have always counted fewer neutrinos than the best models of the sun predict [see "The Solar-Neutrino Problem," by John N. Bahcall; SCIENTIFIC AMERICAN, May 1990].

Super-K has also counted these solar neutrinos, finding only about 50 percent of what is expected. We are studying these data, hoping to find a clear signature of neutrino oscillations. In May the Sudbury Neutrino Observatory in Ontario detected its first neutrinos. It uses 1,000 tons of heavy water, which greatly enhances solar neutrino detection. Other new detectors will start up soon.

An experiment performed at Los Alamos National Laboratory provides a further hint of neutrino oscillation: it detects electron-neutrinos from a source that should produce only muon-neutrinos. The signal is mixed, however, with background processes. The result has not yet been independently confirmed, but some experiments will check it in the next few years.

Mass-induced oscillations between muon- and tau-neutrinos seem the most natural explanation for the Super-K neutrino data, but there are other possibilities. First, the most general scenario has mixing between all three neutrino flavors, and Super-K's data can accommodate some oscillations between electron- and muon-neutrinos at the energies it covers. Yet results from an experiment at the Chooz nuclear power station in Ardennes, France, greatly limit how much electron-muon oscillation could be occurring at Super-K.

Another possibility is that the muon-neutrinos are oscillating to a previously unseen flavor of neutrino. Still, studies of the so-called Z^0 particle at CERN, the European laboratory for particle physics near Geneva, clearly show that there are only three active flavors of neutrino. ("Active" means that the flavor participates in the weak nuclear interaction.) A new flavor would therefore have to be "sterile," a species of neutrino that interacts only through gravity. Some physicists favor this idea, because current evidence for three distinct effects (solar neutrinos, atmospheric neutrinos and the Los Alamos data) cannot be accounted for by one consistent set of masses for the electron-, muon- and tau-neutrinos.

Other oscillation mechanisms, relying on more esoteric effects than neutrino mass, have also been proposed. —E.K., T.K. and Y.T.

The Authors

EDWARD KEARNS, TAKAAKI KAJITA and YOJI TOTSUKA are members of the Super-Kamiokande Collaboration. Kearns, a professor of physics at Boston University, and Kajita, a professor of physics at the University of Tokyo, lead the analysis team that studies proton decay and atmospheric neutrinos in the Super-K data. Totsuka is spokesman for the Super-K Collaboration and is director of the Institute for Cosmic Ray Research at the University of Tokyo, the host institution for the experiment.

Further Reading

THE SEARCH FOR PROTON DECAY. J. M. LoSecco, Frederick Reines and Daniel Sinclair in *Scientific American*, Vol. 252, No. 6, pages 54–62; June 1985.
THE ELUSIVE NEUTRINO: A SUBATOMIC DETECTIVE STORY. Nickolas Solomey. Scientific American Library, W. H. Freeman and Company, 1997.
The Official Super-Kamiokande Web site is available at www-sk.icrr.u-tokyo. ac.jp/doc/sk/
The K2K Long Baseline Neutrino Oscillation Experiment Web site is available at neutrino.kek.jp/
The Super-Kamiokande at Boston University Web site is available at hep.bu. edu/~superk/index.html

ment, we have eliminated any speculation that the anomalous numbers of atmospheric neutrinos could be just a statistical fluke. But it is still important to confirm the effect by looking for the same muon-neutrino oscillation with other experiments or techniques. Different detectors in Minnesota and Italy have provided some verification, but with fewer events measured they do not have the same statistical certainty.

Corroborating Evidence

Further corroboration comes from studies of a different variety of atmospheric neutrino interaction: their collisions with nuclei in the rock around our detector. Electron-neutrinos again produce electrons and subsequent showers of particles, but these are absorbed in the rock and never reach Super-K's cavern. High-energy muon-neutrinos make high-energy muons, which can travel through many meters of rock and enter our detector. We count such muons from upward-traveling neutrinos—downward muons are masked by the background of cosmic-ray muons that penetrate Mount Ikenoyama from above.

We can count upward-traveling muons arriving on trajectories that range from directly up to nearly horizontal. These paths correspond to neutrino travel distances (from production in the atmosphere to the creation of a muon near Super-K) as short as 500 kilometers (the distance to the edge of the atmosphere when looking horizontally) and as long as 13,000 kilometers (the diameter of the earth, looking straight down). We find that the numbers of muon-neutrinos of lower energy that travel a long distance are more depleted than higher-energy muon-neutrinos that travel a short distance. This behavior is just what we expect from oscillations, and careful analysis produces neutrino parameters similar to those from our first study.

If we consider just the three known neutrinos, our data tell us that muon-neutrinos are changing into tau-neutrinos. Quantum theory says that the underlying cause of the oscillation is almost certainly that these neutrinos have mass—although it has been assumed for 70 years that they do not. (The box on the opposite page mentions some other scenarios.)

Unfortunately, quantum theory also limits our experiment to measuring only the difference in mass-squared between the two neutrino components, because that is what determines the oscillation wavelength. It is not sensitive to the mass of either one alone. Super-K's data give a mass-squared difference somewhere between 0.001 and 0.01 electron volt (eV) squared. Given the pattern of masses of other known particles, it is likely that one neutrino is much lighter than the other, which would mean that the mass of the heavier neutrino is in the range of 0.03 to 0.1 eV. What are the implications of this result?

First, giving neutrinos a mass does not wreck the Standard Model. The mismatch between the mass states that make up each neutrino requires the introduction of a set of so-called mixing parameters. A small amount of such mixing has long been observed among quarks, but our data imply that neutrinos need a much greater degree of mixing—an important piece of information that any successful new theory must accommodate.

Second, 0.05 eV is still very close to zero, compared with the masses of the other particles of matter. (The lightest of those is the electron, with a mass of 511,000 eV.) So the long-held belief that neutrinos had exactly zero mass is understandable. But theoreticians who wish to build a Grand Unified Theory, which would elegantly combine all the forces except gravity at enormously high energies, also take note of this relative lightness of neutrinos. They often employ a mathematical device called the seesaw mechanism that actually predicts that such a small but nonzero neutrino mass is very natural. Here the mass of some very heavy particle, perhaps at the Grand Unified mass scale, provides the leverage to separate the very light neutrinos from the quarks and leptons that are a billion to a trillion times heavier.

LONG-BASELINE neutrino oscillation experiments are planned in Japan and the U.S. Beams of neutrinos from accelerators will be detected hundreds of kilometers away. The experiments should confirm the oscillation phenomenon and precisely measure the constants of nature that control it.

Detecting Massive Neutrinos

can diffract, and so on. Furthermore, a particle can be the superposition of two waves. Now suppose that the two waves correspond to slightly different masses. Then, as the waves travel along, the lighter wave gets ahead of the heavier one, and the waves interfere in a way that fluctuates along the particle's trajectory [*see box on opposite page*]. This interference has a musical analogue: the beats that occur when two notes are almost but not exactly the same.

In music this effect makes the volume oscillate; in quantum physics it is the probability of detecting one type of neutrino or another that oscillates. At the outset the neutrino appears as a muon-neutrino with a probability of 100 percent. After traveling a certain distance, it looks like a tau-neutrino with 100 percent probability. At other positions, it could be either a muon-neutrino or a tau-neutrino, depending on the roll of the dice.

This oscillation sounds like bizarre behavior for a particle, but another familiar particle performs similar contortions: the photon, the particle of light. Light can occur in a variety of polarizations, including vertical, horizontal, left circular and right circular. These do not have different masses (all photons are massless), but in certain optically active materials, light with left circular polarization moves faster than right circular light. A photon with vertical polarization is actually a superposition of these two alternatives, and when it is traversing an optically active material its polarization will rotate (that is, oscillate) from vertical to horizontal and so on, as its two circular components go in and out of sync.

For neutrino oscillations of the type we see at Super-K, no "optically active" material is needed; a sufficient mass difference between the two neutrino components will cause flavor oscillations whether the neutrino is passing through air, solid rock or pure vacuum. When a

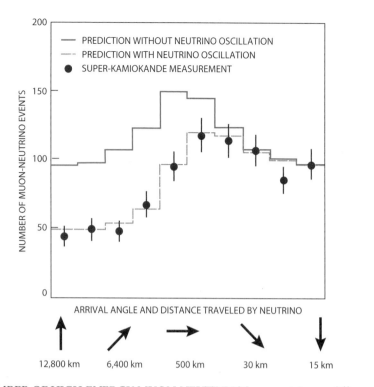

NUMBER OF HIGH-ENERGY MUON-NEUTRINOS seen arriving on different trajectories at Super-K clearly matches a prediction incorporating neutrino oscillations (*green*) and does not match the no-oscillation prediction (*blue*). Upward-going neutrinos (*plotted toward left of graph*) have traveled far enough for half of them to change flavor and escape detection.

neutrino arrives at Super-K, the amount it has oscillated depends on its energy and the distance it has traveled since it was created. For downward muon-neutrinos, which have traveled at most a few dozen kilometers, only a small fraction of an oscillation cycle has taken place, so the neutrinos' flavor is only slightly shifted, and we are nearly certain to detect their original muon-neutrino flavor [*see illustration on page 57*]. The upward muon-neutrinos, produced thousands of kilometers away, have gone through so many oscillations that on average only half of them can be detected as muon-neutrinos. The other half pass through Super-K as undetectable tau-neutrinos.

This description is just a rough picture,

but the arguments based on the ratio of flavors and the up/down event rate are so compelling that neutrino oscillation is now widely accepted as the most likely explanation for our data. We also have done more detailed studies of how the number of muon-neutrinos varies according to the neutrino energy and the arrival angle. We compare the measured number against what is expected for a wide array of possible oscillation scenarios (including no oscillations). The data look quite unlike the no-oscillation expectation but match well with neutrino oscillation for certain values of the mass difference and other physical parameters [*see illustration above*].

With about 5,000 events from our first two years of running the experi-

TIMELINE BY HEIDI NOLAND; AIP EMILIO SEGRÈ VISUAL ARCHIVES (*Pauli and Reines*); COURTESY OF THE INSTITUTE FOR ADVANCED STUDY, PRINCETON (*Davis*); DAVID MALIN Anglo-Australian Observatory (*SN1987A*); ICRR (*Super-Kamiokande*)

LAURIE GRACE

1975–1977
The tau lepton and *b* quark are discovered, revealing a third generation of quarks and leptons.

1983
W and *Z⁰* bosons are discovered at CERN: they are the carriers of the weak force, which mediates neutrino reactions.

1987
Neutrino astronomy: the IMB and Kamiokande proton decay experiments detect 19 neutrinos from Supernova 1987A in the Large Magellanic Cloud.

1989
The Z^0 decay rate is precisely measured at SLAC and CERN, showing there are only three active neutrino generations.

1998
Super-K assembles evidence of neutrino oscillation using atmospheric neutrinos.

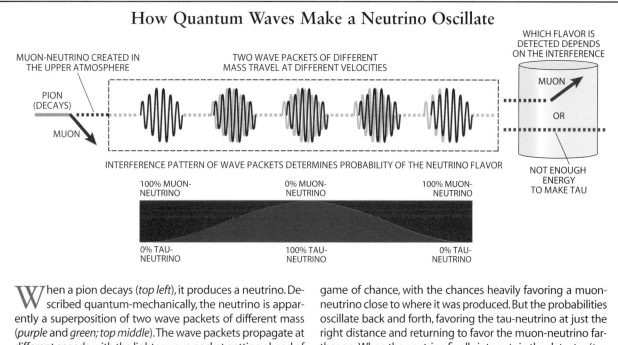

How Quantum Waves Make a Neutrino Oscillate

MUON-NEUTRINO CREATED IN THE UPPER ATMOSPHERE

TWO WAVE PACKETS OF DIFFERENT MASS TRAVEL AT DIFFERENT VELOCITIES

WHICH FLAVOR IS DETECTED DEPENDS ON THE INTERFERENCE

PION (DECAYS)

MUON

MUON

OR

NOT ENOUGH ENERGY TO MAKE TAU

INTERFERENCE PATTERN OF WAVE PACKETS DETERMINES PROBABILITY OF THE NEUTRINO FLAVOR

100% MUON-NEUTRINO	0% MUON-NEUTRINO	100% MUON-NEUTRINO
0% TAU-NEUTRINO	100% TAU-NEUTRINO	0% TAU-NEUTRINO

When a pion decays (*top left*), it produces a neutrino. Described quantum-mechanically, the neutrino is apparently a superposition of two wave packets of different mass (*purple* and *green; top middle*). The wave packets propagate at different speeds, with the lighter wave packet getting ahead of the heavier one. As this proceeds, the waves interfere, and the interference pattern controls what flavor neutrino—muon (*red*) or tau (*blue*)—one is most likely to detect at any point along the flight path (*bottom*). Like all quantum effects, this is a game of chance, with the chances heavily favoring a muon-neutrino close to where it was produced. But the probabilities oscillate back and forth, favoring the tau-neutrino at just the right distance and returning to favor the muon-neutrino farther on. When the neutrino finally interacts in the detector (*top right*), the quantum dice are rolled. If the outcome is muon-neutrino, a muon is produced. If chance favors the tau-neutrino, and the neutrino does not have enough energy to create a tau particle, Super-K detects nothing.   —*E.K., T.K. and Y.T.*

LAURIE GRACE

---

test this surprising conclusion. The clue to our second ratio is to ask how many neutrinos should arrive from each possible direction. Primary cosmic rays fall on the earth's atmosphere almost equally from all directions, with only two effects spoiling the uniformity. First, the earth's magnetic field deflects some cosmic rays, especially the low-energy ones, skewing the pattern of arrival directions. Second, cosmic rays that skim the earth at a tangent make showers that do not descend deep into the atmosphere, and these can develop differently from those that plunge straight in from above.

But geometry saves us: if we "look" up into the sky at some angle from the vertical and then down into the ground at the same angle, we should "see" the same number of neutrinos coming from each direction. Both sets of neutrinos are produced by cosmic rays hitting the atmosphere at the same angle; it is just that in one case the collisions happen overhead and in the other they are partway around the world [*see illustration on preceding page*]. To use this fact, we select neutrino events of sufficiently high energy (so their parent cosmic ray was not deflected by the earth's magnetic field) and then divide the number of neutrinos going up by the number going down. This ratio should be exactly 1 if no neutrinos are changing flavor.

We saw essentially equal numbers of high-energy electron-neutrinos going up and down, as expected, but only half as many upward muon-neutrinos as downward ones. This finding is the second indication that neutrinos are changing identity. Moreover, it provides a clue to the nature of the metamorphosis. The upward muon-neutrinos cannot be turning into electron-neutrinos, because there is no excess of upward electron-neutrinos. That leaves the tau-neutrino. The muon-neutrinos that become tau-neutrinos pass through Super-K without interaction, without detection.

Fickle Flavor

The above two ratios are good evidence that muon-neutrinos are transforming into tau-neutrinos, but why should neutrinos switch flavor at all? Quantum physics describes a particle moving through space by a wave: in addition to properties such as mass and charge, the particle has a wavelength, it

1930
Wolfgang Pauli rescues conservation of energy by hypothesizing an unseen particle that takes away energy missing from some radioactive decays.

1933
Enrico Fermi formulates the theory of beta-decay incorporating Pauli's particle, now called the neutrino, "little neutral one" in Italian.

1956
Frederick Reines (*center*) and Clyde Cowen first detect the neutrino using the Savannah River nuclear reactor.

1962
At Brookhaven, the first accelerator beam of neutrinos proves the distinction between electron-neutrinos and muon-neutrinos.

1969
Raymond Davis, Jr., first measures neutrinos from the sun, using 600 tons of cleaning fluid in a mine in Homestake, S.D.

most tau-neutrinos in the mix will pass through Super-K undetected.

One of the most basic questions experimenters ask is, "How many?" We have built a beautiful detector to study neutrinos, and the first task is simply to count how many we see. Hand in hand with this measurement is the question, "How many did we expect?" To answer that, we must analyze how the neutrinos are produced.

Super-K monitors atmospheric neutrinos, which are born in the spray of particles when a cosmic ray strikes the top of our atmosphere. The incoming projectiles (called primary cosmic rays) are mostly protons, with a sprinkling of heavier nuclei such as helium or iron. Each collision generates a shower of secondary particles, mostly pions and muons, which decay during their short flight through the air, creating neutrinos [*see illustration at right*]. We know roughly how many cosmic rays hit the atmosphere each second and roughly how many pions and muons are made in each collision, so we can predict how many neutrinos to expect.

Tricks with Ratios

Unfortunately, this estimate is only accurate to 25 percent, so we take advantage of a common trick: often the ratio of two quantities can be better determined than either quantity alone. For Super-K, the key is the sequential decay of a pion to a muon and a muon-neutrino, followed by the muon's decay to an electron, an electron-neutrino and another muon-neutrino. No matter how many cosmic rays are falling on the earth's atmosphere, or how many pions they produce, there should be about two muon-neutrinos for every electron-neutrino. The calculation is more complicated than that and involves computer simulations of the cosmic ray showers, but the final predicted ratio is accurate to 5 percent, providing a much better benchmark than the individual numbers of particles do.

After counting neutrinos for almost two years, the Super-K team has found that the ratio of muon-neutrinos to electron-neutrinos is about 1.3 to 1 instead of the expected 2 to 1. Even if we stretch our assumptions about the flux of neutrinos, how they interact with the nuclei and how our detector responds to these events, we cannot explain such a low ratio—unless neutrinos are changing from one type into another.

We can play the ratio trick again to

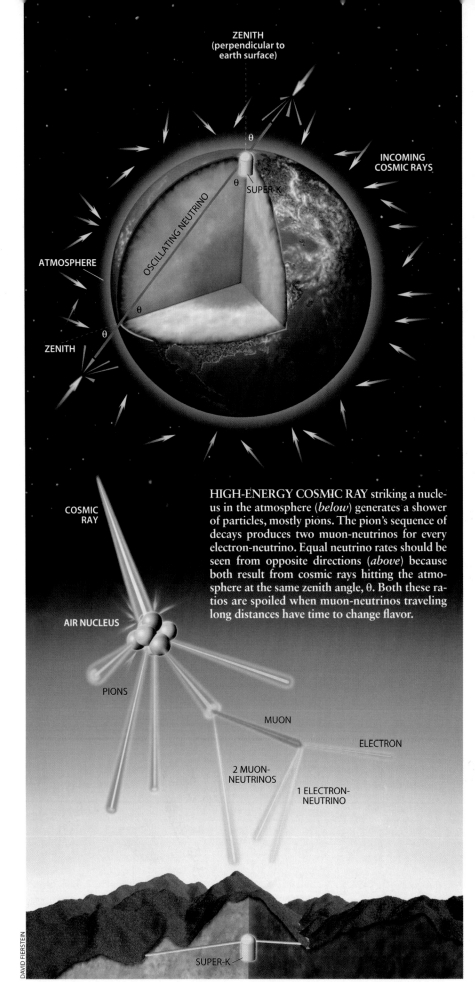

HIGH-ENERGY COSMIC RAY striking a nucleus in the atmosphere (*below*) generates a shower of particles, mostly pions. The pion's sequence of decays produces two muon-neutrinos for every electron-neutrino. Equal neutrino rates should be seen from opposite directions (*above*) because both result from cosmic rays hitting the atmosphere at the same zenith angle, θ. Both these ratios are spoiled when muon-neutrinos traveling long distances have time to change flavor.

DAVID FIERSTEIN

What did the universe look like at the dawn of time? How did it grow and develop into what we live in today? What forms of matter, both mundane and exotic, does it contain?

The recent work has followed two decades of exciting discoveries. In the late 1970s and early 1980s, cosmologists began to map galaxies in a systematic way [see "Superclusters and Voids in the Distribution of Galaxies," by Stephen A. Gregory and Laird A. Thompson; SCIENTIFIC AMERICAN, March 1982]. In so doing, they

sought to measure the distribution of all matter, including the intergalactic "dark matter" that, unlike galaxies, does not give off light. (The assumption that luminous galaxies trace the total mass is no more than an approximation, albeit a constructive one; other research has attempted to quantify the bias that results.)

Cosmo-cartographers discovered that on scales of up to 100 million light-years, galaxies are distributed as a fractal with a dimension of between one and two. The fractal arrangement of matter would be a severe prob-

THREE MILLION GALAXIES, each one containing billions of stars, appear on the map of 15 percent of the sky centered on the constellation Sculptor. Although galaxies fill the sky, making it look roughly the same in every direction, they tend to fall into clusters, clumps and chains. This map, in which the brightness of each dot is proportional to the number of galaxies it repre-

sents, was pieced together by the Automated Plate Measuring Galaxy Survey from black-and-white photographs from the U.K. Schmidt Telescope. On this color-enhanced version, blue, green and red dots depict bright, medium and faint galaxies, respectively. The black patches are areas around bright stars that the survey was unable to probe.

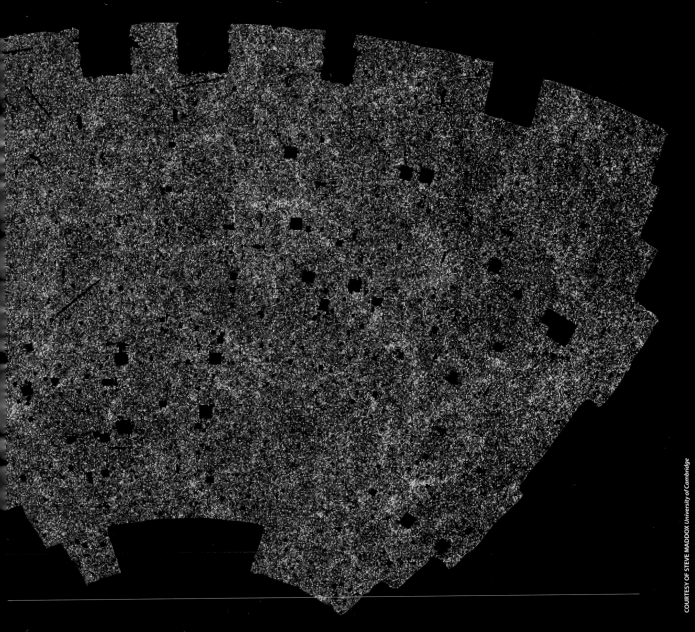

COURTESY OF STEVE MADDOX *University of Cambridge*

10^5 LIGHT-YEARS
GALAXY

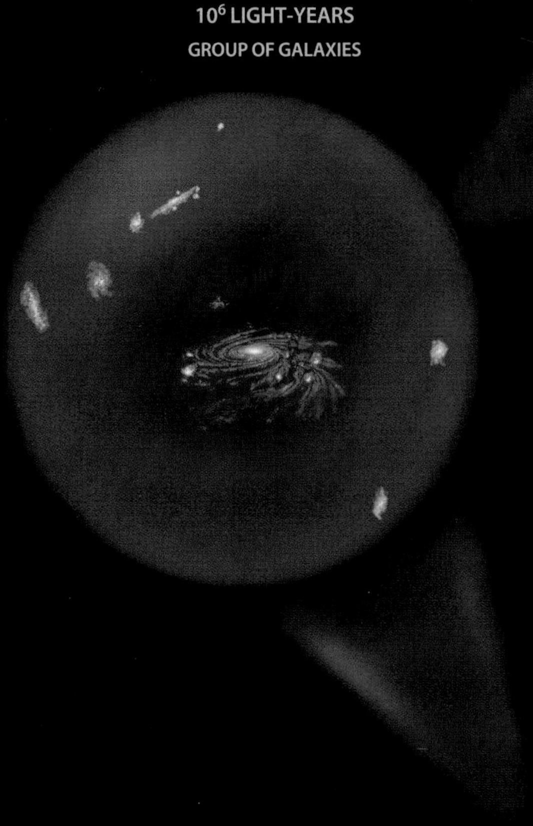

10^6 LIGHT-YEARS
GROUP OF GALAXIES

As the viewer moves out from the Milky Way galaxy to the entire observable universe, clumpiness finally gives way to smoothness. Each sphere is 10 times wider—and therefore 1,000 times more voluminous—than the previous one. A galaxy is a lump of stars, gas, dust and unclassified "dark matter." It agglomerates with other galaxies to form galaxy clusters, the largest bodies in the universe held together by gravity. The clus-

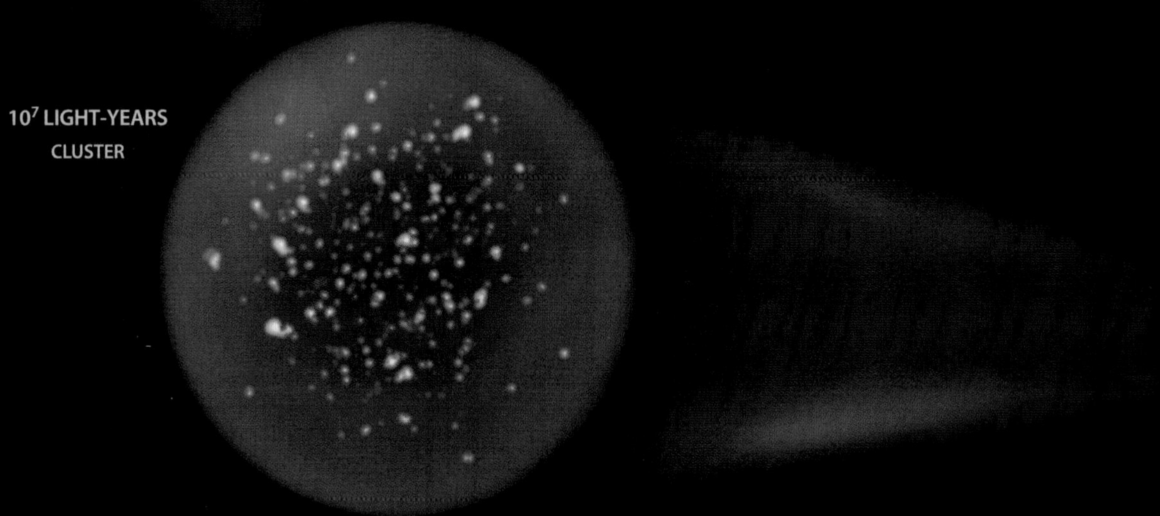

10^7 LIGHT-YEARS
CLUSTER

Large-Scale Structures in the Universe

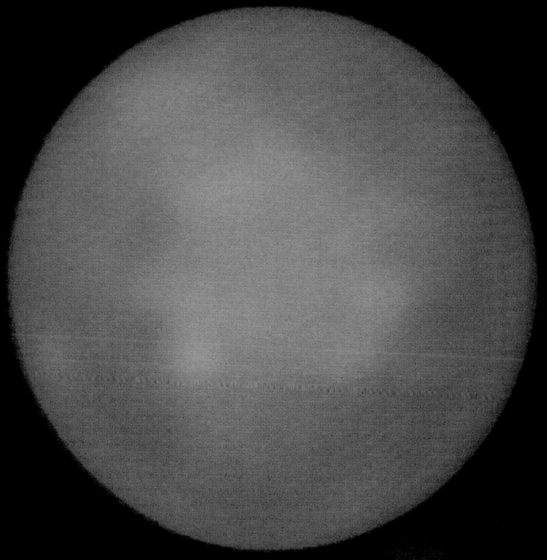

DON DIXON

10¹⁰ LIGHT-YEARS
UNIVERSE

ters, in turn, are clumped together into superclusters and walls, separated by voids of nearly empty intergalactic space. Up to some scale, thought to be around 100 million light-years, these progressively larger structures form a fractal pattern—that is, they are equivalently clumpy on every scale. But between this scale and the size of the observable universe, the clumpiness gives way to near uniformity. —S.D.L.

10⁹ LIGHT-YEARS
WALLS AND VOIDS

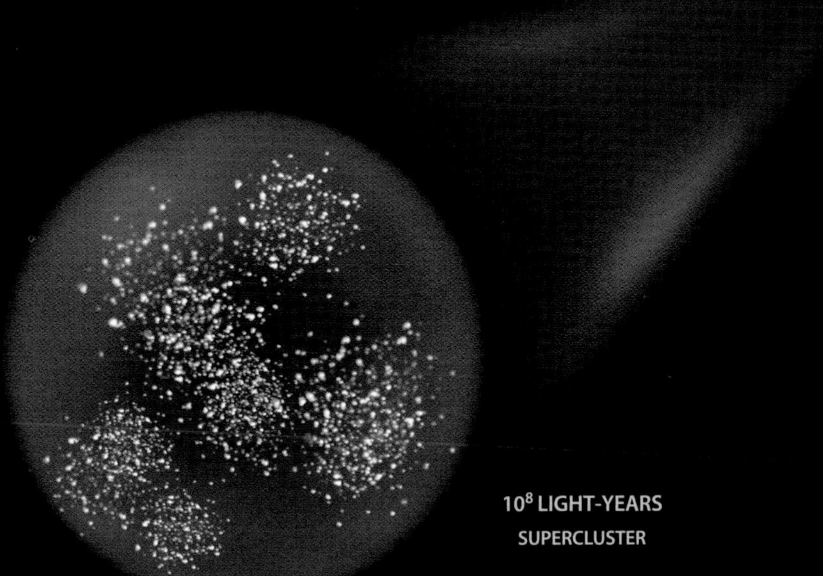

10⁸ LIGHT-YEARS
SUPERCLUSTER

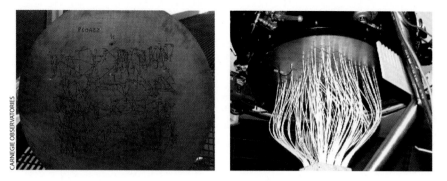

TO SPEED UP THE SURVEY of more than 26,000 galaxies, Stephen A. Shectman designed an instrument capable of measuring 112 galaxies simultaneously. In a metal plate (*far left*), he drilled holes that corresponded to the positions of the galaxies in the sky. Fiber-optic cables (*near left*) carried the light from each galaxy down to a separate channel on a spectrograph at the 2.5-meter du Pont telescope at the Carnegie Observatories on Cerro Las Campanas in Chile.

lem for the cosmological principle if it extended to larger scales, because a fractal distribution is never homogeneous and isotropic. Unlike, say, a crowd of people, a fractal does not approach homogeneity when viewed from a distance; like a coastline, it looks uneven on every scale. In a fractal universe of dimension two, the expected mass within a spherical volume centered on a random galaxy would increase as the square of the radius instead of the cube. In such a universe, the mean density would be a function of scale, and other universal parameters such as the cosmic expansion rate would lose their meaning. In short, the fractal findings seemed to pull the rug out from under modern cosmology.

Subsequent surveys, however, indicated that on scales of hundreds of millions of light-years, the fractal nature broke down. The broader distribution of galaxies could be described in terms of a simple statistical process with a well-defined mean and variance—a noise process. The cosmological principle was saved. But in the late 1980s new problems rose to threaten it [see "Very Large Structures in the Universe," by Jack O. Burns; SCIENTIFIC AMERICAN, July 1986]. A high-resolution survey detected a "Great Wall" of galaxies 750 million light-years long, more than 250 million light-years wide and 20 million light-years thick. A noise process could not readily explain such a colossal, coherent structure. These discoveries motivated still larger mapping projects, including the Las Campanas Redshift Survey that my colleagues and I conducted from 1988 to 1994.

Slicing through the Universe

Because the Las Campanas survey sought to measure the distribution of galaxies on a scale several times that of previous studies, it encountered a number of observational challenges. The most distant galaxies were faint, so photographing them would require a lengthy exposure time. The large survey volume increased the number of objects that had to be observed. In sum, we had to observe more objects with a longer exposure but with only limited telescope time. For these reasons, we decided to construct a survey that would be very deep (out to two billion light-years) and wide (85 degrees across the sky) but thin (1.5 degrees)—effectively sampling the galaxy distribution in only two dimensions. Though thinness compromised the signal, it allowed a first glimpse of the organization of the cosmos on scales of several billion light-years.

The survey made six separate maps and recorded the positions of more than 26,000 galaxies. The data were collected at the Carnegie Observatories on Cerro Las Campanas in the Atacama Desert of Chile. This information was analyzed by Stephen A. Shectman of the Carnegie Observatories, Robert P. Kirshner and Huan Lin of the Harvard-Smithsonian Center for Astrophysics, Augustus Oemler and Douglas L. Tucker of Yale University, Paul L. Schechter of the Massachusetts Institute of Technology and me.

The survey involved several steps. First, we made photometric observations—basically, highly sensitive photographs of the sky—with a charge-coupled device (CCD) camera mounted on the one-meter Swope telescope at Las Campanas. For maximum efficiency, we used a specialized technique known as drift-scan photometry, in which we pointed the telescope at the beginning of a survey field and then turned off its automated drive. The telescope stood still as the sky drifted past. Computers read information from the CCD detector at exactly the same rate as the rotation of the earth, producing one long, continuous image at a constant celestial latitude. Completing the photometry took a total of 450 hours.

Second, we analyzed the strips to determine which objects were likely to be galaxies and suitable for inclusion into the survey. Candidates were chosen based on their brightness and galaxylike fuzziness. Finally, we observed these objects with a spectrograph at the 2.5-meter du Pont telescope at Las Campanas. The spectrograph broke the light down into a spectrum of colors, from which we calculated each galaxy's redshift, a measure of its distance.

Because gathering enough light to measure the spectrum of a galaxy in this survey took about two hours, if we had observed only one galaxy at a time, a survey of this size would have been impossible. But Shectman designed a multiple fiber-optic system to measure the spectra of 112 galaxies simultaneously. This system worked as follows: Once we had chosen the prospective galaxies, we drilled holes in a metal plate to be mounted at the focus of the telescope. These holes corresponded to the positions of the galaxies in the sky. Into these holes we plugged fiber-optic cables that carried the light from each galaxy down to a separate channel on the spectrograph. Even with this parallel processing, it took us 600 hours of observing time over 100 nights to measure all the spectra.

Sounding Out the Universe

Looking at the maps produced by the survey, the eye is struck by the sense that the galaxies are not randomly distributed but instead tend to bunch together [*see illustration on page 69*]. Yet one must be careful of visual impressions. Our brains often seek patterns where none exist. In this case, however, statistical techniques bear out the existence of clustering.

The simplest way to measure clustering is to use correlation functions, which represent the number of pairs of objects as a function of their separation. For example, the distribution of deer in a forest is highly clustered on small scales—say, a few

Mapping the Universe

tens of yards. In randomly picking out deer in the forest, you would notice that you are much more likely to find another deer a few yards away than a few hundred yards away. The correlation function would show a strong positive signal on the scale of a few tens of yards and a weak or negative signal on the scale of a few hundred yards. It mathematically describes the well-known fact that deer tend to travel in small groups.

A similar analysis can be done on galaxies, and it works well on scales that are much smaller than the size of a survey. But on larger scales it is not very informative. The problem is that the number of galaxies—and therefore the number of galaxy pairs—is set. If there is an excess of pairs at small separations, there must be a deficit of pairs at larger separations, because the total number of pairs is fixed. This zero sum game contaminates the clustering signal on larger scales.

Fortunately, a complementary technique can reliably measure clustering at large scales: harmonic analysis, also known as power spectrum analysis. Harmonic analysis, as its name suggests, is closely allied to the study of sound. In fact, the mathematical analysis of the distribution of galaxies and of random noise is identical. (The power spectrum is conceptually related to but physically distinct from the kind of spectrum that astronomers usually study, that of light.)

Many common phenomena, such as the waves on the surface of the sea and the air pressure fluctuations in a room, are most naturally described in terms of their power spectra. In fact, the human ear performs a similar analysis on pressure fluctuations—that is, sound. The fluctuations can be thought of as a collection of pure tones, each with a certain strength. The cochleas in our ears decompose the fluctuations into their constituent tones (or frequencies). The signal sent to the brain describes the strength (or amplitude) of each tone.

The power spectrum is a measure of the strength of the pressure fluctuations as a function of frequency. It is what the graphic equalizer of a stereo displays. Large musical instruments, such as a bass or a tuba, put out a large fraction of their power at long wavelengths, which correspond to low frequencies. The sound of breaking glass consists primarily of high frequencies.

Random noise is special because it can be completely described in terms of its power spectrum [see Mathematical Games, by Martin Gardner; SCIENTIFIC AMERICAN, April 1978]. Consider two people who go to visit the same waterfall several minutes apart. Each records several minutes of sound. Although their recordings will not be the same—the sound made by the waterfall is always changing—both will record the characteristic sound of the waterfall. If the observers take their recordings and perform a harmonic analysis, they will each find the same power spectrum. The statistical properties of their two recordings are identical.

The Color of Sound

Noise with a flat power spectrum, corresponding to equal power at all frequencies, is called white noise. The term comes from an analogy with color. Each color has a different frequency; if you add all the colors together equally, you get white. In terms of sound, white noise is the static between radio stations. Its sound is perfectly random; at each instant the sound is unrelated to, or uncorrelated with, the sound that came before. Another special power spectrum is that of pink noise, in which each octave delivers the same power [see illustration below]. A waterfall produces pink noise.

Harmonic analysis can reconcile the cosmological principle with the clustering of matter. If the universe is homogeneous and isotropic, observers sitting on planets in separate galaxies should measure the same properties for the universe on its largest scales. Of course, they will see different galaxy distributions, just as any two slices in the Las Campanas survey are different. But given enough surveys, or a survey of sufficient size, the two observers should measure the same statistical fluctuations. These fluctuations, like those of the sound of a waterfall, can be described in terms of the power spectrum.

As the universe expands and evolves, various physical processes modify the power spectrum of its large-scale structure. Cosmologists generally believe that quantum-mechanical fluctuations imparted the initial power spectrum shortly after the start of the big bang. In the late 1960s English physicist Edward R. Harrison and Russian physicist Yakov B. Zel'dovich derived a shape for this primordial power spectrum—namely, a power law with the functional form of frequency to the negative third power, a pink-noise spectrum in three dimensions.

Harrison and Zel'dovich both reasoned that most natural forces, including gravity, have no intrinsic length scale; they are power laws. Therefore, the initial power spectrum should be some form of power law in frequency, so it does not single out any particular length scale. They also grasped the role of the horizon size in the evolution of the universe. The horizon size is simply the distance a beam of light could have traveled in the universe since the big bang up to any particular moment. Because the influence of gravity also travels at the speed of light, two points in the universe can interact gravitationally only if they are separated by a distance less than or equal to the horizon size. As the universe ages, the horizon size grows. Therefore, the horizon size defines a natural length scale over which gravity can operate.

What Harrison and Zel'dovich realized was that if the initial power-law spectrum was not precisely frequency to the

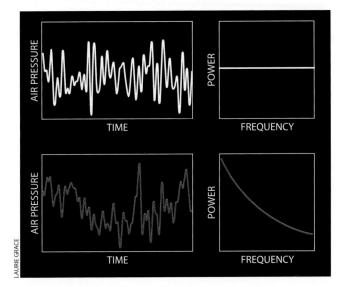

WHITE AND PINK NOISE surround us. White noise, the grating sound of static on a badly tuned radio or television, is completely random. The sound fluctuates from instant to instant without any pattern (*top*). Pink noise, the sound of a waterfall or waves crashing on the beach, is fractal (*bottom*). This distinction is reflected in the power spectra (*graphs at right*): white noise has equal power at all frequencies, but pink noise has more power in the bass than in the treble, in inverse proportion to the frequency.

negative third power, then one of two things would occur. If the power law were steeper—say, frequency to the negative fourth power—then fluctuations on very small scales would have been greater. In calculating the density fluctuations in the early history of the universe, when the horizon size was small, they found that many regions would have contained such a high density of matter that they would have quickly collapsed, filling the cosmos with black holes. Fortunately, this did not happen. Our very existence rules out such a power spectrum. On the other hand, if the power law were shallower, then at later times the density on large scales would fluctuate hugely. No such fluctuations exist.

Although this argument is quite persuasive to cosmologists, it does not explain how such a spectrum would have arisen. Cosmological inflation provides an explanation, which was an early success for the theory, as well as being one of its few testable consequences [see "The Inflationary Universe," by Alan H. Guth and Paul J. Steinhardt; SCIENTIFIC AMERICAN, May 1984].

A Great Number of Great Walls

The power spectrum of the universe today is very different from the primordial Harrison-Zel'dovich spectrum. Gravity has amplified the initial fluctuations and led to the growth of such structures as clusters of galaxies. At earlier times, the growth of fluctuations on specific scales was enhanced or retarded depending on whether the universe was dominated by matter or by radiation and whether elementary particles were light and fast-moving or heavy and slow-moving. One of the great challenges for modern cosmology is to determine how the initial power spectrum evolved into the spectrum observed today. Only in the past several years have observations, such as those of galaxy distribution and of the cosmic microwave background radiation, acquired enough data to put theories to the test.

So-called cold dark matter models are now the most popular explanations for the growth of structure. Their premise is that most of the mass in the universe resides in some unseen (hence, "dark"), relatively massive type of particle. It is "cold" because, being heavy, it travels slowly. The particle, which would interact with ordinary matter only through the force of gravity, could also account for the missing mass in galaxies and galaxy clusters [see "Dark Matter in the Universe," by Lawrence M. Krauss; SCIENTIFIC AMERICAN, December 1986].

One of the surprising results from our survey is its deviation from the cold dark matter model on scales of around 600 million light-years. At smaller scales the predictions of the model match our findings, but something strange singles out the large scales [see illustration at right]. Previous surveys had suggested such a discrepancy, and one of the principal results of Las Campanas has been to substantiate it. From the strength of the deviation and the size of the survey, we calculated the probability of seeing such a deviation purely by chance as one in several thousand.

What is very interesting about this deviation is that it can be traced back to the huge structures seen in the galaxy distribution [see illustration on opposite page]. These structures are defined by the sharp boundaries, filaments and voids in the galaxy maps. The largest are almost three billion light-years across, several times the size of the Great Wall. The association of these walls and voids with the deviation in the

power spectrum is a crucial finding of the Las Campanas survey. It means that on this scale, the galaxy distribution cannot be fully characterized using the mathematics of random noise. Some other physical process must have acted to imprint this characteristic scale on the density fluctuations.

In fact, this inconsistency is what allows these walls and voids to properly be called structures. With a pure-noise process, walls and voids would occasionally appear by chance. But they would be much rarer, in keeping with the statistics of noise. They would be statistical fluctuations or chance superpositions, rather than true structures.

What could be responsible for the mammoth walls and voids? Gravity might be a good explanation except that it causes smaller-scale fluctuations to collapse more quickly, simply because it takes less time for gravity to pull matter together on small scales. If gravity were the culprit, galaxy clustering should have begun on small scales and then worked its way up to large scales. For the past two decades, such a bottom-up scenario, known as hierarchical clustering, has been the paradigm for explaining structure on scales smaller than about 150 million light-years. Yet the deviations in our survey begin to appear at much larger scales. Hierarchical clustering may still apply on the small scales, but it cannot explain the walls and voids on the larger scales.

The New Music of the Spheres

Several hypotheses have emerged, although none can yet be reconciled with all the data. The first is a hot dark matter scenario wherein the universe is dominated by light, fast-moving particles such as neutrinos. The result would be a top-down progression in structure formation starting on large scales. Unfortunately, this theory has the side effect of washing out structure on small scales, so it fails to account for the small-scale galaxy clustering.

A second hypothesis posits that the universe is less dense than cosmologists suppose. Most of this decrease in density comes at the expense of exotic dark matter. Ordinary particles such as protons and electrons thus have a proportionately greater influence. They would have constituted a viscous fluid in the

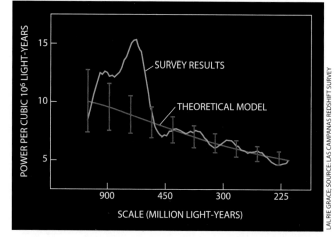

POWER SPECTRUM of the cosmos, as measured by the Las Campanas survey (*blue line*), generally follows the prediction of the cold dark matter model (*pink*). But the power increases dramatically on scales of 600 million to 900 million light-years. This discrepancy means that the universe is much clumpier on those scales than current theories can explain.

Mapping the Universe

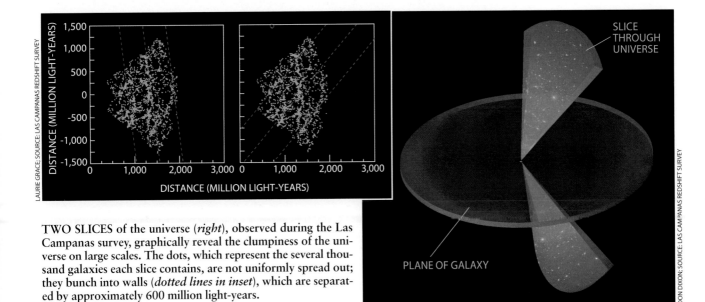

TWO SLICES of the universe (*right*), observed during the Las Campanas survey, graphically reveal the clumpiness of the universe on large scales. The dots, which represent the several thousand galaxies each slice contains, are not uniformly spread out; they bunch into walls (*dotted lines in inset*), which are separated by approximately 600 million light-years.

early universe. Before the universe was cool enough for the protons and electrons to combine and form atoms, sound waves reverberated through this fluid. When the protons and electrons recombined, the acoustic waves gave a boost to the gravitational collapse on certain scales. Intriguingly, an underdense universe would also resolve other cosmological conundrums [see "Inflation in a Low-Density Universe," by Martin A. Bucher and David N. Spergel; SCIENTIFIC AMERICAN, January].

A third hypothesis points out that 600 million light-years is roughly the horizon distance at the time when the average density of matter in the universe overtook that of radiation. Such a profound change would presumably have affected the power spectrum somehow. Whatever the final explanation, it may be that astronomers are detecting the largest unique length scale associated with any physical process in nature.

Even a survey the size of Las Campanas contains only about 50 independent measurements of the power spectrum at these large scales. Larger surveys are needed, and several are now either in the development stages or under way. An Anglo-Australian consortium called the 2DF Survey is mapping more than a quarter-million galaxies. Soon the American-Japanese Sloan Digital Sky Survey will begin to measure the distances to almost one million galaxies over half of the sky, sampling a volume 20 times greater than that of the Las Campanas survey.

These studies are not the first use of harmonic analysis in the history of astronomy. It was originally Pythagoras in the sixth century B.C. who applied musical analysis to the motion of the sun, moon, stars and planets. He believed that the celestial bodies were holes in a set of crystal spheres through which shone the celestial light. The motions of these spheres, he reasoned, must produce sounds. Their distances and their speeds must be in the same ratios as musical harmonies. This was the first "music of the spheres."

In the 17th century Johannes Kepler, before formulating his famous laws of celestial motion, believed that the orbits of the planets could be described in terms of heavenly spheres inscribed between the five perfect Pythagorean solids. He reasoned that the harmonious ratios of music might be derived from these solids, and thus he argued for a fundamental relation between the orbits of the planets and these harmonies. This was the second music of the spheres.

Today our notion of harmonic analysis is quite different. It is based on analyzing the harmonic components of random distributions, and the sound is more like the gush of a waterfall than that of divine instruments. Although this modern endeavor may seem neither as pleasing nor as spiritual as those of the past, the concept of an isotropic universe wedded with an understanding of random fields now allows us once again to hear the music of the spheres. SA

The Author

STEPHEN D. LANDY first became interested in cosmology when he was lost in the woods one night and had nothing to do but stare up at the stars. After receiving his Ph.D. in physics from Johns Hopkins University in 1994, he did postdoctoral research work at the Carnegie Observatories in Pasadena, Calif., and at the University of California, Berkeley. Currently he is a visiting scientist at the College of William and Mary.

Further Reading

PRINCIPLES OF PHYSICAL COSMOLOGY. P.J.E. Peebles. Princeton University Press, 1993.
THE TWO-DIMENSIONAL POWER SPECTRUM OF THE LAS CAMPANAS REDSHIFT SURVEY: DETECTION OF EXCESS POWER ON 100 H^{-1} MPC SCALES. Stephen D. Landy et al. in *Astrophysical Journal Letters*, Vol. 456, pages L1–L4; January 1, 1996. Preprint available at xxx.lanl.gov/abs/astro-ph/9510146 on the World Wide Web.
THE LAS CAMPANAS REDSHIFT SURVEY. Stephen A. Shectman et al. in *Astrophysical Journal*, Vol. 470, pages 172–188; October 10, 1996. Preprint available at xxx.lanl.gov/abs/astro-ph/9604167 on the World Wide Web.
THE LARGE-SCALE SMOOTHNESS OF THE UNIVERSE. Kelvin K. S. Wu, Ofer Lahav and Martin J. Rees in *Nature*, Vol. 397, pages 225–230; January 21, 1999.
The Las Campanas Redshift Survey site is available at manaslu.astro.utoronto.ca/~lin/lcrs.html on the World Wide Web.
The Sloan Digital Sky Survey site is available at www.sdss.org on the World Wide Web.

The Evolution of Galaxy

by J. Patrick Henry, Ulrich G. Briel and Hans Böhringer

The royal Ferret of Comets was busy tracking his prey. On the night of April 15, 1779, Charles Messier watched from his Paris observatory as the Comet of 1779 slowly passed between the Virgo and Coma Berenices constellations on its long journey through the solar system. Messier's renown in comet spotting had inspired the furry moniker from King Louis XV, but on this night he took his place in astronomy history books for a different reason. He noticed three fuzzy patches that looked like comets yet did not move from night to night; he added them to his list of such impostors so as

not to be misled by them during his real work, the search for comets. Later he commented that a small region on the Virgo-Coma border contained 13 of the 109 stationary splotches that he, with the aid of Pierre Mechain, eventually identified—the Messier objects well known to amateur and professional astronomers today.

As so often happens in astronomy, Messier found something completely different from what he was seeking. He had discovered the first example of the most massive things in the universe held together by their own gravity: clusters of galaxies. Clusters are assem-

blages of galaxies in roughly the same way that galaxies are assemblages of stars. On the cosmic organizational chart, they are the vice presidents—only one level below the universe itself. In fact, they are more massive relative to a human being than a human being is relative to a subatomic particle.

In many ways, clusters are the closest that astronomers can get to studying the universe from the outside. Because a cluster contains stars and galaxies of every age and type, it represents an average sample of cosmic material—including the dark matter that choreographs the movements of celestial objects yet

WILLIAM A. BAUM *University of Washington*; HUBBLE SPACE TELESCOPE WFPC TEAM AND SPACE TELESCOPE SCIENCE INSTITUTE

Clusters

TWO BRIGHT GALAXIES in the Coma cluster, one elliptical (*top left*) and the other spiral (*top right*), appear in this composite Hubble Space Telescope image taken in 1994. The Coma cluster, located some 300 million light-years away, was one of the first galaxy clusters identified by astronomers. Most of the other splotches in the image are galaxies at even greater distances.

The most massive objects in the universe are huge clusters of galaxies and gas that have slowly congregated over billions of years. The process of agglomeration may now be ending

cannot be seen by human eyes. And because a cluster is the result of gravity acting on immense scales, its structure and evolution are tied to the structure and evolution of the universe itself. Thus, the study of clusters offers clues to three of the most fundamental issues in cosmology: the composition, organization and ultimate fate of the universe.

A few years after Messier's observations in Paris, William Herschel and his sister, Caroline, began to examine the Messier objects from their garden in England. Intrigued, they decided to search for others. Using substantially better telescopes than their French predecessor had, they found more than 2,000 fuzzy spots—including 300 in the Virgo cluster alone. Both William and his son, John, noticed the lumpy arrangement of these objects on the sky. What organized these objects (which we now know to be galaxies) into the patterns they saw?

A second question emerged in the mid-1930s, when astronomers Fritz Zwicky and Sinclair Smith measured the speeds of galaxies in the Virgo cluster and in a slightly more distant cluster in Coma. Just as the planets orbit about the center of mass of the solar system, galaxies orbit about the center of mass of their cluster. But the galaxies were orbiting so fast that their collective mass could not provide enough gravity to hold them all together. The clusters had to be nearly 100 times as heavy as the visible galaxies, or else the galaxies would have torn out of the clusters long ago. The inescapable conclusion was that the clusters were mostly made of unseen, or "dark," matter. But what was this matter?

These two mysteries—the uneven distribution of galaxies in space and the unknown nature of dark matter—continue to confound astronomers. The former became especially puzzling after the discovery in the mid-1960s of the cosmic microwave background radiation. The radiation, a snapshot of the universe after the big bang and before the formation of stars and galaxies, is almost perfectly smooth. Its tiny imperfections somehow grew to the structures that exist today, but the process is still not clear [see "Very Large Structures in the Universe," by Jack O. Burns; SCIENTIFIC AMERICAN, July 1986]. As for

dark matter, astronomers have learned a bit more about it since the days of Zwicky. But they are still in the uncomfortable position of not knowing what most of the universe is made of [see "Dark Matter in the Universe," by Lawrence M. Krauss; SCIENTIFIC AMERICAN, December 1986].

Light from Dark Matter

Impelled by these mysteries, the pace of discovery in the study of clusters has accelerated over the past 40 years. Astronomers now know of some 10,000 of them. American astronomer George Abell compiled the first large list in the early 1950s, based on photographs of the entire northern sky taken at Palomar Observatory in California. By the 1970s astronomers felt they at least understood the basic properties of clusters: They consisted of speeding galaxies bound together by huge amounts of dark matter. They were stable and immutable objects.

Then came 1970. In that year a new satellite, named Uhuru ("freedom" in Swahili) in honor of its launch from Kenya, began observing a form of radiation hitherto nearly inaccessible to astronomers: x-rays. Edwin M. Kellogg, Herbert Gursky and their colleagues at American Science and Engineering, a small company in Massachusetts, pointed Uhuru at the Virgo and Coma clusters. They found that the clusters consist not only of galaxies but also of huge amounts of gas threading the space between the galaxies. The gas is too tenuous to be seen in visible light, but it is so hot—more than 25 million degrees Celsius—that it pours out x-rays.

In short, astronomers had found some of the dark matter—20 percent of it by mass. Although the gas is not enough to solve the dark matter mystery completely, it does account for more mass than all the galaxies put together. In a way, the term "clusters of galaxies" is inaccurate. These objects are balls of gas in which galaxies are embedded like seeds in a watermelon

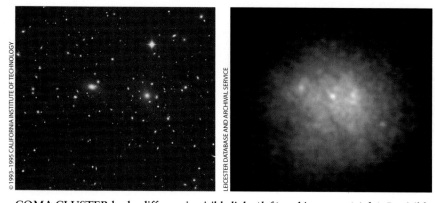

COMA CLUSTER looks different in visible light (*left*) and in x-rays (*right*). In visible light, it appears to be just an assemblage of galaxies. But in x-rays, it is a gargantuan ball of hot gas some five million light-years across.

[see "Rich Clusters of Galaxies," by Paul Gorenstein and Wallace Tucker; SCIENTIFIC AMERICAN, November 1978].

Since the early 1970s, the x-ray emission has been scrutinized by other satellites, such as the Einstein X-Ray Observatory, the Roentgen Satellite (ROSAT) and the Advanced Satellite for Cosmology and Astrophysics (ASCA). Our own research mainly uses ROSAT. The first x-ray telescope to record images of the entire sky, ROSAT is well suited for observations of large diffuse objects such as clusters and is now engaged in making detailed images of these regions. With this new technology, astronomers have extended the discoveries of Messier, Zwicky and the other pioneers.

When viewed in x-rays, the Coma cluster has a mostly regular shape with a few lumps [*see left illustration on page 74*]. These lumps appear to be groups of galaxies—that is, miniature clusters.

One lump to the southwest is moving into the main body of the cluster, where other lumps already reside. Virgo, by comparison, has an amorphous shape. Although it has regions of extra x-ray emission, these bright spots are coming from some of the Messier galaxies rather than from clumps of gas [*see right illustration on page 74*]. Only the core region in the northern part of Virgo has a nearly symmetrical structure.

Such x-ray images have led astronomers to conclude that clusters form from the merger of groups. The lumps in the main body of the Coma cluster presumably represent groups that have already been drawn in but have not yet been fully assimilated. Virgo seems to be in an even earlier stage of formation. It is still pulling in surrounding material and, at the current rate of progress, will look like Coma after a few billion years. This dynamic view of clusters gobbling up

and digesting nearby matter is in stark contrast to the static view that astronomers held just a few years ago.

Taking Their Temperature

Ever since astronomers obtained the first good x-ray images in the early 1980s, they have wanted to measure the variation of gas temperature across clusters. But making these measurements is substantially more difficult than making images, because it requires an analysis of the x-ray spectrum for each point in the cluster. Only in 1994 did the first temperature maps appear.

The maps have proved that the formation of clusters is a violent process. Images of the cluster Abell 2256, for example, show that x-ray emission has not one but rather two peaks. The western peak is slightly flattened, suggesting that a group slamming into the main cluster has swept up material just as a snowplow does. A temperature map supports this interpretation [*see illustration on opposite page*]. The western peak, it turns out, is comparatively cool; its temperature is characteristic of the gas in a group of galaxies. Because groups are smaller than clusters, the gravitational forces within them are weaker; therefore, the speed of the gas molecules within them—that is, their temperature—is lower. A typical group is 50 trillion times as massive as the sun and has a temperature of 10 million degrees C. By comparison, a typical cluster weighs 1,000 trillion suns and registers a temperature of 75 million degrees C; the heaviest known cluster is five

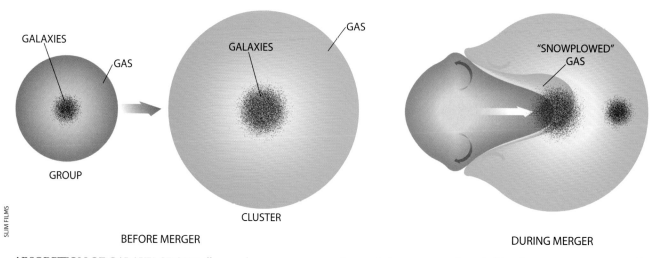

BEFORE MERGER

DURING MERGER

ABSORPTION OF GALAXY GROUP allows a cluster to grow to colossal size. Pulled in by gravity, the group slams into the cluster, pushing gas out the sides. The galaxies themselves pass through the cluster, their progress unimpeded by the tenuous gas. Eventually the galaxies and gas mix together, forming a unified cluster that continues to draw in other groups until no more are to be found.

The Evolution of Galaxy Clusters

times as massive and nearly three times as hot.

Two hot regions in Abell 2256 appear along a line perpendicular to the presumed motion of the group. The heat seems to be generated as snowplowed material squirts out the sides and smashes into the gas of the main cluster. In fact, these observations match computer simulations of merging groups. The group should penetrate to the center of the cluster in several hundred million years. Thus, Abell 2256 is still in the early stages of the merger.

The late stages of a merger are apparent in another cluster, Abell 754. This cluster has two distinguishing features. First, optical photographs show that its galaxies reside in two clumps. Second, x-ray observations reveal a bar-shaped feature from which the hot cluster gas fans out. One of the galaxy clumps is in the bar region, and the other is at the edge of the high-temperature region to the west.

Theorists can explain this structure with an analogy. Imagine throwing a water balloon, which also contains some pebbles, into a swimming pool. The balloon represents the merging group: the water is gas, and the pebbles are galaxies. The swimming pool is the main cluster. When the balloon hits the water in the pool, it ruptures. Its own water stays at the surface and mixes very slowly, but the pebbles can travel to the other side of the pool. A similar process apparently took place in Abell 754. The gas from the merging group was suddenly stopped by the gas of the cluster, while the group galaxies passed right through the cluster to its far edge.

A third cluster, Abell 1795, shows what a cluster looks like billions of years after a merger. The outline of this cluster is perfectly smooth, and its temperature is nearly uniform, indicating that the cluster has assimilated all its groups and settled into equilibrium. The exception is the cool region at the very center. The lower temperatures occur because gas at the center is dense, and dense gas emits x-rays more efficiently than tenuous gas. If left undisturbed for two or three billion years, dense gas can radiate away much of its original energy, thereby cooling down.

As the gas cools, substantial amounts of lukewarm material build up—enough for a whole new galaxy. So where has all this material gone? Despite exhaustive searches, astronomers have yet to locate conclusively any pockets of tepid gas. That the cluster gas is now losing

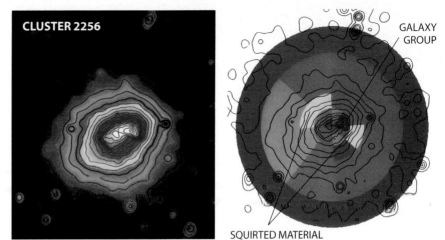

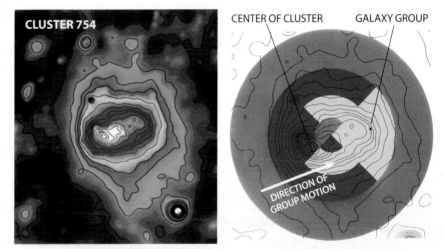

THREE GALAXY CLUSTERS are at different stages in their evolution, as shown in these x-ray images (*left column*) and temperature maps (*right column*). The first cluster, Abell 2256, is busily swallowing a small group of galaxies, which is identified by its relatively low temperature. On the map red is comparatively cool, orange intermediate and yellow hot.

The second cluster, Abell 754, is several hundred million years further along in its digestion of a galaxy group. The hapless group probably entered from the southeast, because the cluster is elongated in that direction. The galaxies of the group have separated from their gas and passed through the cluster.

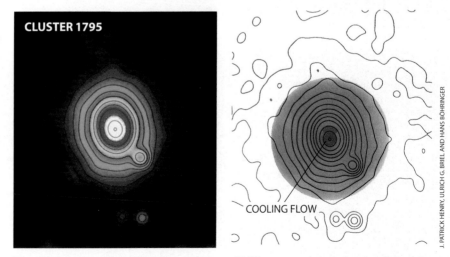

The third cluster, Abell 1795, has gone several billion years since its last meal. Both its x-ray brightness and gas temperature are symmetrical. At the core of the cluster is a cool spot, a region of dense gas that has radiated away much of its heat.

J. PATRICK HENRY, ULRICH G. BRIEL AND HANS BOHRINGER

From Cluster Evolution to Cosmic Evolution

Ever since the big bang, the universe has been expanding. All objects not bound to one another by gravity or some other force are being pulled apart. But will the cosmic expansion continue forever, or will the gravity of all the matter in the universe be sufficient to halt it? Traditional attempts to answer the question have foundered because they require a careful census of the total amount of matter in the universe—and that is difficult, because most of it is invisible dark matter.

Now there is a new approach made possible by studying the evolution of galaxy clusters. Over time, clusters grow as they accrete matter, until the matter within their gravitational reach is exhausted. The more matter there is, the faster and bigger they can grow (*right*). If the universe has enough matter to come to a halt, then fewer than 10 percent of the massive clusters that exist today were in place four billion years

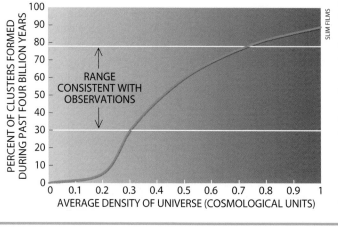

ago—and new clusters should still be forming and growing today. But if the universe has only one quarter of the matter needed to stop its expansion, then all the massive clusters were in place four billion years ago—and no further growth has taken place since then.

The observed cluster evolution rate favors the latter scenario: because galaxy clusters have essentially stopped growing, there must be comparatively little matter in the universe. Therefore, the cosmos will expand forever (unless there exists material with exotic physical properties, such as a gravitational repulsion that varies with time). Other recent measurements of cosmic expansion, using distant supernovae and other markers, agree. Although the case is not closed, several independent pieces of evidence now make it more likely that astronomers do know the ultimate fate of the cosmos. —*J.P.H.*

---

heat is obvious from the temperature maps. Perhaps the heat loss started only fairly recently, or perhaps the collision of galaxy groups prevents cool gas from collecting in one spot. These so-called cooling flows remain yet another unsolved mystery.

Bottoms Up

The sequence represented by these three Abell clusters is probably undergone by every cluster as it grows. Galaxy groups occasionally join the cluster; with each, the cluster gains hot gas, bright galaxies and dark matter. The extra mass creates stronger gravitational forces, which heat the gas and accelerate the galaxies. Most astronomers believe that almost all cosmic structures agglomerated in this bottom-up way. Star clusters merged to form galaxies, which in turn merged to form groups of galaxies, which are now merging to form clusters of galaxies. In the future it will be the clusters' turn to merge to form still larger structures. There is, however, a limit set by the expansion of the universe. Eventually, clusters will be too far apart to merge. Indeed, the cosmos may be approaching this point already.

By cosmological standards, all the above-mentioned clusters (Coma, Virgo, and Abell 2256, 754 and 1795) are

nearby objects. Astronomers' efforts to understand their growth are analogous to understanding human growth from a single photograph of a crowd of people. With a little care, you could sort the people in the picture into the proper age sequence. You could then deduce that as people age, they generally get taller, among other visible changes.

You could also study human growth by examining a set of photographs, each

containing only people of a certain age—for example, class pictures from grade school, high school and college. Similarly, astronomers can observe clusters at ever increasing distances, which correspond to ever earlier times. On average, the clusters in a more distant sample are younger than those in a nearby one. Therefore, researchers can piece together "class photos" of clusters of different ages. The advantage of this approach is

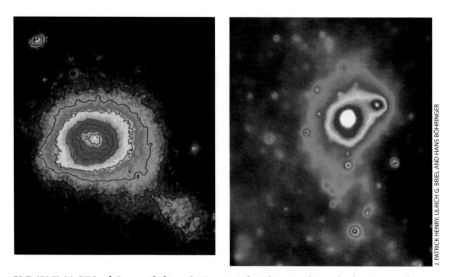

X-RAY IMAGES of Coma (*left*) and Virgo (*right*) clusters show the hot intergalactic gas that dominates the luminous part of these structures. The gas in Coma has a more regular shape than that in Virgo, suggesting that the cluster has reached a more advanced stage of formation. Both clusters are surrounded by infalling material.

The Evolution of Galaxy Clusters

that it lets astronomers work with a whole sample of clusters, rather than just a few individual clusters. The disadvantage is that the younger objects are too far away to study in detail; only their average properties can be discerned.

One of us (Henry) applied this method to observations from the ASCA x-ray satellite. He found that distant, younger clusters are cooler than nearby, older ones. Such a temperature change shows that clusters become hotter and hence more massive over time—further proof of the bottom-up model. From these observations researchers have estimated the average rate of cluster evolution in the universe. The rate, which is related to the overall evolution of the universe and to the nature of the dark matter, implies that the universe will expand forever [*see box on opposite page*].

New x-ray observations may shed light on the remaining dark matter in clusters. By the end of 2000 there will be three advanced x-ray observatories in orbit: the Advanced X-Ray Astrophysics Facility from the U.S., the X-ray Multi-mirror Mission from Europe and ASTRO-E from Japan.

In the meantime, observations of another form of radiation, known as extreme ultraviolet light, are yielding mysteries of their own. The extreme ultraviolet has an energy that is only slightly lower than that of x-rays. It is heavily absorbed by material in our galaxy, so astronomers assumed that most clusters are not visible in this wavelength band. But recently Richard Lieu of the Uni-

versity of Alabama at Huntsville, C. Stuart Bowyer of the University of California at Berkeley and their colleagues studied five clusters using the sensitive Extreme Ultraviolet Explorer satellite.

These clusters, they discovered, shine brightly in the extreme ultraviolet. In some ways, this discovery was as unexpected as the first detection of x-rays from clusters in the early 1970s. Although some of the radiation comes from the same gas that generates the x-rays, there appears to be an additional source in at least some of the clusters. This finding is very new and has not yet been explained. Perhaps astronomers are

seeing another component of the clusters' dark matter for the first time. The upcoming x-ray facilities may identify this new component.

Those of us involved in this work feel a special bond with Charles Messier as he strained to glimpse those faint patches of light in Virgo, not knowing their true significance. As advanced as our technology has become, we still strain to understand these clusters. We feel a bond with future observers as well, for science advances in a continuous process of small increments. We have been helped by those who preceded us; we share our new understanding with those who follow. **SA**

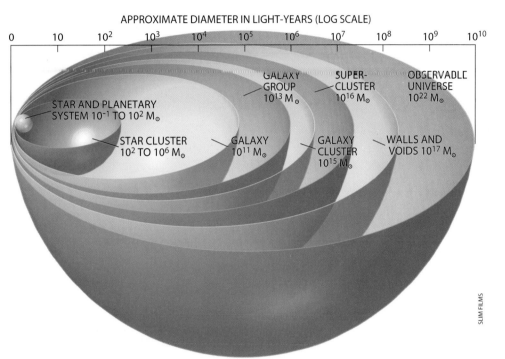

APPROXIMATE DIAMETER IN LIGHT-YEARS (LOG SCALE)

STAR AND PLANETARY SYSTEM 10^{-1} TO 10^2 $M_\odot$

STAR CLUSTER 10^2 TO 10^6 $M_\odot$

GALAXY GROUP 10^{13} $M_\odot$

SUPER-CLUSTER 10^{16} $M_\odot$

OBSERVABLE UNIVERSE 10^{22} $M_\odot$

GALAXY 10^{11} $M_\odot$

GALAXY CLUSTER 10^{15} $M_\odot$

WALLS AND VOIDS 10^{17} $M_\odot$

SLIM FILMS

HIERARCHY OF COSMIC STRUCTURES ranges from stars and planets to the universe itself. The largest objects held together by gravity are galaxy clusters with masses up to 10^{15} times that of the sun (denoted as $M_\odot$). Although there is a higher level of organization consisting of superclusters and great walls, these patterns are not bound gravitationally. On even larger scales, the universe is featureless. Astronomers think most of these structures form from the progressive agglomeration of smaller units.

The Authors

J. PATRICK HENRY, ULRICH G. BRIEL and HANS BÖHRINGER are x-ray astronomers who study clusters of galaxies. The first two met in the late 1970s while working at the Smithsonian Astrophysical Observatory on one of the instruments on the Einstein X-ray Observatory satellite. Henry is now an astronomy professor at the University of Hawaii. He says he enjoys sitting on his lanai and thinking about large-scale structure while watching the sailboats off Diamond Head. Briel and Böhringer are staff members of the Max Planck Institute for Extraterrestrial Physics in Garching. Briel is an observer who tested and calibrated the ROSAT instrument that made the temperature maps discussed in this article. Böhringer is a theorist who studies galaxy clusters, cosmology and the interstellar medium.

Further Reading

X-RAY EMISSION FROM CLUSTERS OF GALAXIES. Craig L. Sarazin. Cambridge University Press, 1988.
CLUSTERS AND SUPERCLUSTERS OF GALAXIES. Edited by A. C. Fabian. Kluwer Academic Publishers, 1992.
STORMY WEATHER IN GALAXY CLUSTERS. Jack O. Burns in *Science*, Vol. 280, pages 400–404; April 1998.
AN X-RATED VIEW OF THE SKY. Joshua N. Winn in *Mercury*, Vol. 27, No. 1, pages 12–16; January/February 1998.

For student exercises relating to this article, please see the back of this reader

A New Look at Quasars

Recent observations from the Hubble Space Telescope
may reveal the nature and origin of quasars,
the mysterious powerhouses of the cosmos

by Michael Disney

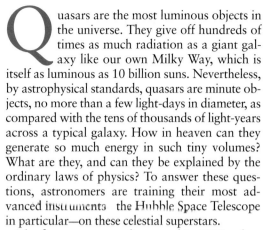

Quasars are the most luminous objects in the universe. They give off hundreds of times as much radiation as a giant galaxy like our own Milky Way, which is itself as luminous as 10 billion suns. Nevertheless, by astrophysical standards, quasars are minute objects, no more than a few light-days in diameter, as compared with the tens of thousands of light-years across a typical galaxy. How in heaven can they generate so much energy in such tiny volumes? What are they, and can they be explained by the ordinary laws of physics? To answer these questions, astronomers are training their most advanced instruments the Hubble Space Telescope in particular—on these celestial superstars.

The first quasar was discovered in 1962, when Cyril Hazard, a young astronomer at the University of Sydney, began to study a powerful source of radio waves in the Virgo constellation. Hazard could not pinpoint the source, because the radio telescopes of the time were not precise enough, but he realized that the moon would occult the unknown object when it passed through Virgo. So he and John Bolton, the director of a newly built radio telescope in Parkes, Australia, pointed the instrument's giant dish toward the radio source and waited for the moon to block it out. By timing the disappearance and reappearance of the signal, they would be able to pinpoint the source of radio emissions and identify it with a visible object in the sky. Unfortunately, by the time the moon arrived the great dish was tipped so far over that it was running into its safety stops. Apparently unperturbed by the risk, Bolton sheared off the stops so that the telescope could follow the occultation downward until the rim of the dish almost touched the ground.

His daring was to be rewarded. From their measurements Hazard was able to calculate the first accurate position for such a cosmic radio source and then identify it with a comparatively bright, starlike object in the night sky. The position of that object—dubbed 3C273—was sent to Maarten Schmidt, an astronomer at the Mount Palomar Observatory in California, who had the honor of taking its optical spectrum. After some initial puzzlement, Schmidt realized he was looking at the

DON DIXON

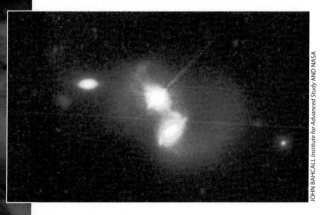

GALACTIC COLLISIONS may sometimes result in the birth of a quasar. A massive black hole at the core of one of the galaxies sucks in stars and gas from the other galaxy, and the maelstrom of infalling matter generates a beam of intense radiation. Such a process may be occurring in quasar PG 1012+008 (*inset*), as observed by the Hubble Space Telescope. The quasar is 1.6 billion light-years from the earth.

JOHN BAHCALL *Institute for Advanced Study* AND NASA

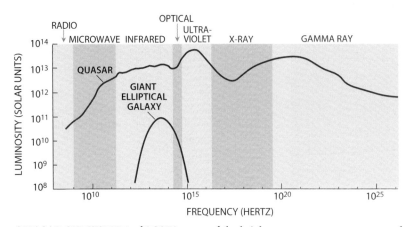

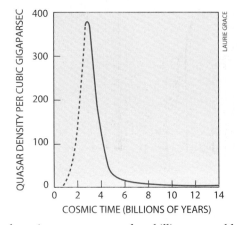

QUASAR SPECTRUM of 3C273—one of the brightest quasars and the first to be discovered—is far broader than the spectrum of a typical giant elliptical galaxy (*left*). In the optical range, the quasar is hundreds of times more luminous. Quasars were most numerous when the universe was two to four billion years old (*right*). Today quasars are 1,000 times less common. Quasars were also rare in the very early history of the universe, but the exact numbers are uncertain.

spectrum of hydrogen shifted redward by the expansion of the universe. The 16 percent redshift meant that 3C273 was about two billion light-years from the earth. Given the distance and the observed brightness of the object, Schmidt calculated that it had to be emitting several hundred times more light than any galaxy. The first quasistellar radio source—or quasar—had been discovered.

Spurred by Hazard's and Schmidt's work, astronomers identified many more quasars in the following years. Observers discovered that the brightness of many quasars varied wildly; some grew 10 times as bright in just a matter of days. Because no object can turn itself on and off in less time than it takes for light to travel across it, the astonishing implication was that these highly luminous objects must be a mere light-week or so across. Some reputable as-

tronomers refused to believe that the enormous distances and luminosities implied by the redshifts could be so great. The controversy spilled over to the popular press, where it attracted a younger generation of scientists, like myself, into astronomy.

Since then, astronomers have catalogued thousands of quasars, some with redshifts as large as 500 percent. They are not difficult to find, because unlike stars, and unlike galaxies composed of stars, they emit radiation of all energies from gamma rays to radio. Ironically, the radio emissions by which they were first discovered turn out to be, in energetic terms, the least significant portion of their output. For that reason, some astronomers argue that the name "quasar" should be superseded by QSO, for quasistellar object.

There are four big questions facing

the quasar astronomer. First, how are quasars related to galaxies and stars? Second, how long does each quasar pour out its enormous energy? In our immediate cosmic neighborhood—within one billion light-years from the earth—there is only one quasar for every million galaxies. But that does not necessarily mean that quasars are much rarer than galaxies; they could be just as common but have much shorter luminous lifetimes. This brings us to the third question: Why were quasars far more numerous in the past? At a redshift of 200 percent—about 10 billion light-years away—the number of quasars jumps 1,000-fold. In the early universe, apparently, quasars were 1,000 times more common than they are today. And last, the most perplexing question: How do quasars generate their prodigious energy?

None of these questions can be easily

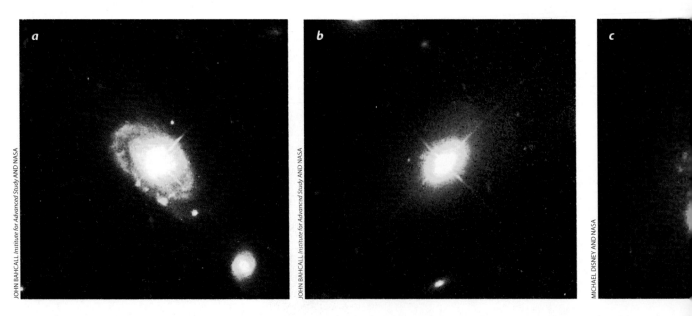

A New Look at Quasars

answered. The typical quasar is so far from the earth that its image on the largest ground-based optical telescope would be 100 million times too small to be resolved. From the outset, one school of astronomers felt that quasars had to be sited in galaxies, probably in their nuclei. They gathered evidence to show that all the phenomena observed in quasars were manifested, albeit in a far weaker form, in the nuclei of about 1 percent of the giant galaxies near the Milky Way. A whole zoo of active galactic nuclei were revealed, including radio galaxies, Seyferts, blazars, optically violent variables, superluminal sources and so on. But astronomers could not tell whether these objects were separate classes of galactic nuclei or representations of the same phenomenon viewed from different angles or at different stages of development. Nor could astronomers explain the exact relation between the active galactic nuclei and quasars. Critics of the theory linking the two types of objects argued that the luminosity of the active nuclei did not even approach that of quasars. And the sheer power of quasars is their most distinctive and mysterious characteristic.

A more direct approach was taken by Jerry Kristian, another astronomer at Mount Palomar, in 1973. He argued that if quasars were inside giant host galaxies, then the images of the closest quasars should show a fuzzy halo of light from the stars in the host galaxy. It would not be an easy observation, because light from the brilliant quasar, scattered by the earth's atmosphere, would swamp the light from the much fainter host. Nevertheless, Kristian was

able to demonstrate that the lowest red-shift quasars did exhibit this faint, fuzzy halo. His evidence was not very satisfactory, though, because virtually nothing could be discerned about the host galaxies, not even whether they were elliptical or spiral.

Troubles with Hubble

When the Hubble Space Telescope was proposed in the mid-1970s, most quasar observers expected it to provide the first clear images of host galaxies, if they really existed. Indeed, finding host galaxies became one of the primary objectives of the telescope. We on the European space telescope team designed the Hubble's Faint Object Camera with quasars very much in mind. For instance, we built in a high-magnification focus and a coronograph specially designed to block off the brilliant light from quasars and thus make the surrounding hosts more visible.

By then, astronomers suspected that the only way a quasar could produce so much energy out of such a tiny volume was if the object contained a massive black hole at its core. Such a monster hole, weighing as much as a billion suns, would suck in all the gas and stars in its vicinity. Gas would swirl into the hole at almost the speed of light, generating intense magnetic fields and huge amounts of radiation. Donald Lynden-Bell, then an astronomer at the California Institute of Technology, calculated that a massive black hole could convert up to 40 percent of the infalling matter's rest-mass energy into radiation. Such a process would be 400 times more effi-

cient than the production of thermonuclear energy in stars. For this reason, massive black holes became the favored theoretical explanation for quasars. (All the other plausible models would rapidly evolve into black holes anyway.)

One problem with the model, though, was explaining how these monsters could be fed. A black hole of such enormous mass would tend to swallow up all the nearby stars and gas and then go out for lack of fuel. To explore this mystery, the European space telescope team also built a special long-slit spectrograph into the Faint Object Camera. This instrument was designed to measure the rotation speed of material in active galactic nuclei and thus weigh the putative black holes at their cores.

After the much delayed launch of Hubble in 1990, it was soon discovered that the telescope's main mirror had been incorrectly manufactured. The images were such a travesty that quasar astronomers were devastated. I, for one, felt that five to 10 of the most productive years of my astronomical life had been thrown away through unforgivable incompetence. And many others felt likewise. To its credit, however, the National Aeronautics and Space Administration had designed Hubble to be repairable, and astronauts installed new cameras with corrective optics in 1993. Unfortunately, none of the special instruments in the original cameras for observing quasars was recoverable. If we were still going to search for quasar host galaxies, we would have to use the new Wide-Field Planetary Camera, which was not designed for the job. Nevertheless, two teams set out to try: a European team headed by myself and an American team led by astronomer John Bahcall of the Institute for Advanced Study in Princeton, N.J.

Observing quasar hosts with the Hubble's new camera was akin to looking into the headlights of an oncoming car in a snowstorm and trying to identify its

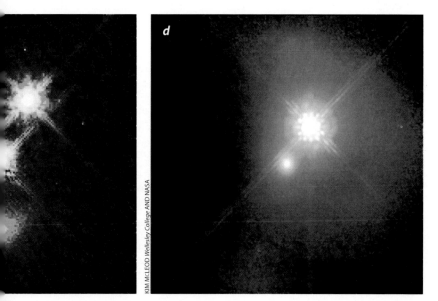

HOST GALAXIES surround most of the quasars observed by the Hubble Space Telescope. The spiral galaxy around PG 0052+251 (*a*) and the elliptical galaxy around PHL 909 (*b*) appear to be undisturbed by collisions. But a galactic crash seems to be fueling IRAS 04505-2958 (*c*). A spiral ring torn from one of the galaxies is below the quasar; the object above it is a foreground star. Hubble's new infrared camera observed another galactic smashup (*d*). The dots around quasar PG 1613+658 were caused by diffraction; the colliding galaxy is below it and to the left.

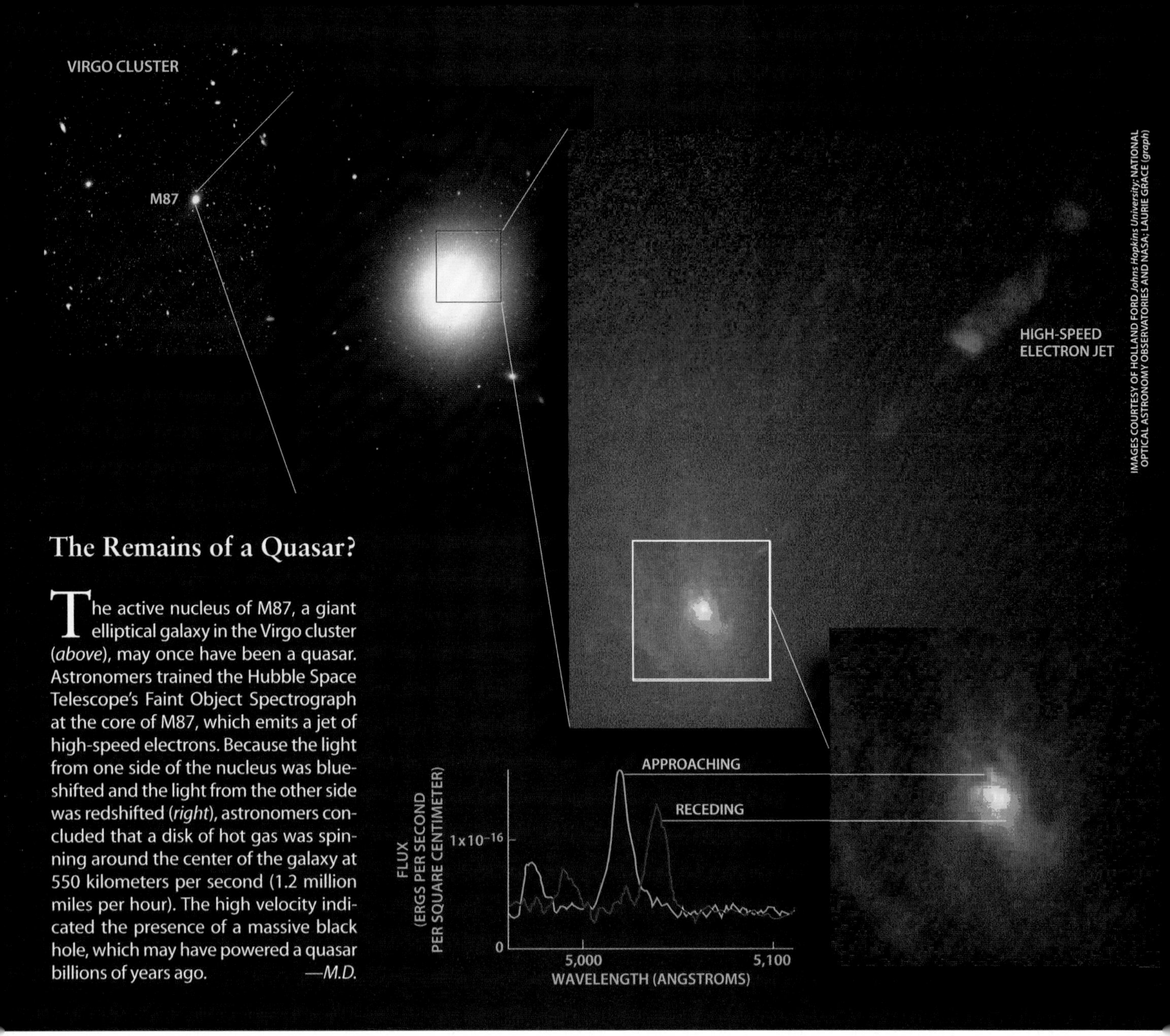

VIRGO CLUSTER
M87
HIGH-SPEED
ELECTRON JET
APPROACHING
RECEDING
FLUX
(ERGS PER SECOND
PER SQUARE CENTIMETER)
1x10−16
0
5,000
5,100
WAVELENGTH (ANGSTROMS)

IMAGES COURTESY OF HOLLAND FORD *Johns Hopkins University*; NATIONAL OPTICAL ASTRONOMY OBSERVATORIES AND NASA; LAURIE GRACE (*graph*)

The Remains of a Quasar?

The active nucleus of M87, a giant elliptical galaxy in the Virgo cluster (*above*), may once have been a quasar. Astronomers trained the Hubble Space Telescope's Faint Object Spectrograph at the core of M87, which emits a jet of high-speed electrons. Because the light from one side of the nucleus was blueshifted and the light from the other side was redshifted (*right*), astronomers concluded that a disk of hot gas was spinning around the center of the galaxy at 550 kilometers per second (1.2 million miles per hour). The high velocity indicated the presence of a massive black hole, which may have powered a quasar billions of years ago. —*M.D.*

manufacturer. Astronomers had to take several shots of each object, subtract the high beam—the light from the quasar—and play with the remaining images on their computers. In most cases, the final result contained enough detail to make out a galactic structure. Sadly, Jerry Kristian, who pioneered this field, was killed in an ultralight airplane crash in California just before the Hubble results were published.

What did the space telescope reveal? Of the 34 quasars observed, about 75 percent showed the faint, fuzzy halo indicating a host galaxy. The remaining 25 percent showed no such halo, but it is possible that the quasar's dazzling beam is blocking the image in those cases. About half of the host galaxies were elliptical, and half were spiral. The quasars with the strongest radio signals were located primarily in elliptical galaxies, but no other patterns were discernible. Most intriguing, about three quarters of the host galaxies appeared to be colliding with or swallowing other galaxies.

This finding had already been reported by John Hutchings and his co-workers at Dominion Astrophysical Observatory in Victoria, Canada, who had used a ground-based telescope with adaptive optics to observe quasars. But the Hubble, with its greater resolution, provided much more vivid evidence of the galactic interactions. The images suggest that colliding galaxies supply the fuel for the quasar's energy production. Stars and gas shaken loose by the violence of the impact may be funneling into a massive black hole at the heart of one of the galaxies. The infalling matter then generates the intense radiation.

This process would explain the relative numbers of quasars at different stages in the universe's history. Immediately after the big bang, there were no galaxies and hence no galactic collisions. Even if black holes existed then, there was no mechanism to funnel material toward them and turn them into quasars. Consequently, few quasars are observed at very high redshifts—that is, more than 11 billion years ago. But in the following aeons, galaxies began to assemble and collide, producing the relatively large number of quasars observed 10 billion light-years from the earth. Finally, the expansion of the universe carried most galaxies away from one another, reducing the number of galactic collisions—and the number of quasars.

Nevertheless, about one quarter of the host galaxies observed by Hubble—such as the spiral galaxy surrounding the quasar PG 0052+251—show no sign that they are colliding with another galaxy. It is possible that a faint companion galaxy is present in these cases, but the quasar's beam is preventing astronomers from seeing it. Or perhaps there is an alternative mechanism that can provide enough fuel to transform a massive black hole into a quasar. What we do know for certain is that the vast majority of galactic interactions do *not* seem to produce quasars; if they did, quasars would be far more common than we observe.

The scarcity of quasars seems to suggest that massive black holes are a rare phenomenon, absent from most galaxies. But this supposition is contradicted by recent evidence gathered by a team of astronomers led by Douglas Richstone of the University of Michigan. Combining observations from Hubble with spectroscopic evidence from ground-based telescopes, the team weighed the nuclei of 27 of the galaxies closest to the Milky Way. In 11 of the galaxies Richstone's group found convincing evidence for the presence of massive dark bodies, most likely black holes.

Furthermore, some of those massive black holes may once have been quasars. In 1994 a group of astronomers led by Holland Ford of Johns Hopkins University used Hubble to look into the heart of M87, a giant elliptical galaxy in the Virgo cluster, about 50 million light-years from the earth. The active nucleus of M87 emits a broad spectrum of radiation, similar to the radiation produced by a quasar but with only a thousandth the intensity. The astronomers discovered that the light from one side of the nucleus was blueshifted (indicating that the source is speeding toward the earth), whereas light from the other side was redshifted (indicating that the source is speeding away). Ford concluded that they were observing a rotating disk of hot gas. What is more, the disk was spinning so rapidly that it could be bound together only by a black hole weighing as much as three billion suns—the same kind of object that is believed to be the quasar's power source. Billions of years ago the nucleus of M87 may well have been a quasar, too.

The Quasar Quest

The recent observations have led astronomers to construct a tentative theory to explain the origin of quasars. According to the theory, most galaxies contain massive black holes capable of generating vast amounts of energy under very special circumstances. The energy production rises dramatically when gas and stars start falling into the black holes at an increased rate, typically about one solar mass a year. This huge infall occurs most often, but not always, as a result of galactic collisions or near misses. Quasars were thus far more prevalent in the epoch of high galaxy density, when the universe was younger and more crowded than it is now.

What can be said of the individual lifetimes of these beasts? Not much for certain. The observed host galaxies show no evidence that the quasars have been radiating long enough to damage them. The hydrogen gas in the host galaxies, for example, has not been substantially ionized, as it might be if quasars were long-lived. The observation that so many of the host galaxies are interacting—and the fact that such interactions typically last for one galactic rotation period or less—indicates a quasar lifetime shorter than 100 million years. And if the existence of massive black holes in most galaxies implies a past epoch of quasarlike activity in each case, then the small number of observed quasars—only one for every 1,000 galaxies during their most abundant era—suggests a quasar lifetime of 10 million years or less. If that number is correct, the quasar phenomenon is but a transient phase in the 10-billion-year lifetime of a galaxy. And although the amount of energy generated by each quasar is tremendous, it would account for only about 10 percent of the galaxy's lifetime radiant output.

Obviously, more observations are needed to test the theory. The Hubble Space Telescope must be trained on a wider sample of nearby quasars to search for host galaxies. The existing samples of nearby quasars are too small and too narrowly selected for reliable conclusions to be drawn, and the distant host galaxies are too difficult to observe with the current instruments.

Astronomers expect to make new discoveries with the help of two devices recently installed on Hubble: the Near Infrared Camera and Multi-Object Spectrometer (NICMOS), which will allow scientists to peer into the nuclei of galaxies obscured by clouds of dust, and the Space Telescope Imaging Spectrograph (STIS), which has already demonstrated its usefulness by detecting and weighing a black hole in a nearby galaxy in one fortieth the time it would have taken previously. In 1999 NASA plans to install the Advanced Camera, which will contain a high-resolution coronograph of the kind that was always needed to block the overwhelming quasar light and unmask the host galaxies.

On the theoretical side, we need to understand how and when massive black holes formed in the first place. Did they precede or follow the formation of their host galaxies? And we would like a convincing physical model to explain exactly how such black holes convert infalling matter into all the varieties of quasar radiation, from gamma rays to superluminal radio jets. That may not be easy. Astronomer Carole Mundell of Jodrell Bank Observatory in England once remarked that observing quasars is like observing the exhaust fumes of a car from a great distance and then trying to figure out what is going on under the hood. **SA**

The Author

MICHAEL DISNEY is a professor of astronomy at the University of Wales in Cardiff, U.K. For 20 years he was a member of the European Space Agency's Space Telescope Faint Object Camera team. He received his Ph.D. from University College London in 1968. His other scientific interests include hidden galaxies, bird flight and the environmental dangers posed by oil supertankers.

Further Reading

PERSPECTIVES IN ASTROPHYSICAL COSMOLOGY. Martin J. Rees. Cambridge University Press, 1995.
ACTIVE GALACTIC NUCLEI. Ian Robson. John Wiley, 1996.
AN INTRODUCTION TO ACTIVE GALACTIC NUCLEI. Bradley Peterson. Cambridge University Press, 1997.
Information on the Hubble Space Telescope is available at http://www.stsci.edu on the World Wide Web.

Gamma-Ray Bursts

New observations illuminate the most powerful explosions in the universe

by Gerald J. Fishman and Dieter H. Hartmann

ALFRED T. KAMAJIAN

About three times a day our sky flashes with a powerful pulse of gamma rays, invisible to human eyes but not to astronomers' instruments. The sources of this intense radiation are likely to be emitting, within the span of seconds or minutes, more energy than the sun will in its entire 10 billion years of life. Where these bursts originate, and how they come to have such incredible energies, is a mystery that scientists have been attacking for three decades. The phenomenon has resisted study—the flashes come from random directions in space and vanish without trace—until very recently.

On February 28, 1997, we were lucky. One such burst hit the Italian-Dutch Beppo-SAX satellite for about 80 seconds. Its gamma-ray monitor established the position of the burst—prosaically labeled GRB 970228—to within a few arc minutes in the Orion constellation, about halfway between the stars Alpha Tauri and Gamma Orionis. Within eight hours, operators in Rome had turned the spacecraft around to look in the same region with an x-ray telescope. They found a source of x-rays (radiation of somewhat lower frequency than gamma rays) that was fading fast, and they fixed its location to within an arc minute.

Never before has a burst been pinpointed so accurately and so quickly, allowing powerful optical telescopes, which have narrow fields of view of a few arc minutes, to look for it. Astronomers on the Canary Islands, part of an international team led by Jan van Paradijs of the University of Amsterdam and the University of Alabama in Huntsville, learned of the finding by electronic mail. They had some time available on the 4.2-meter William Herschel Telescope, which they had been using to study the locations of other bursts. They took a picture of the area 21 hours after GRB 970228. Eight days later they looked again and found that a spot of light seen in the earlier photograph had disappeared.

On March 13 the New Technology Telescope in La Silla, Chile, took a long, close look at those coordinates and discerned a diffuse, uneven glow. The Hubble Space Telescope later resolved it to be a bright point surrounded by a somewhat elongated background object. In a few days the Hubble reexamined the position and still found the point—now very faint—as well as the fuzzy glow, unaltered. Many of us believe the latter to be a galaxy, but its true identity remains unknown.

Even better, on the night of May 8, Beppo-SAX operators located a 15-second burst, designated GRB 970508. Soon after, Howard E. Bond of the Space Telescope Science Institute in Baltimore photographed the region with the 0.9-meter optical telescope on Kitt Peak in Arizona; the next night a point of light in the field had actually brightened. Other telescopes confirm that after becoming most brilliant on May 10, the source began to fade. This is the first time that a burst has been observed reaching its optical peak—which, astonishingly, lagged its gamma-ray peak by a few days.

Also for the first time, on May 13 Dale Frail, using the Very Large Array of radio telescopes in New Mexico, detected radio emissions from the burst remnant. Even more exciting, the primarily blue spectrum of this burst, taken on May 11 with the Keck II telescope on Hawaii, showed a few dark lines, apparently caused by iron and magnesium in an intervening cloud. Astronomers at the California Institute of Technology find that the displacement of these absorption lines indicates a distance of more than seven billion light-years. If this interpretation holds up, it will establish that bursts occur at cosmological distances. In that case, gamma-ray bursts must represent the most powerful explosions in the universe.

Confounding Expectations

For those of us studying gamma-ray bursts, this discovery salves two recent wounds. In November 1996 the Pegasus XL launch vehicle failed to release the High Energy Transient Explorer (HETE) spacecraft equipped with very accurate instruments for locating gamma-ray bursts. And in December the Russian Mars '96 spacecraft, with several gamma-ray detectors, fell into the Pacific Ocean after a rocket malfunction. These payloads were part of a set designed to launch an attack on the origins of gamma-ray bursts. Of the newer satellites equipped with gamma-ray instruments, only Beppo-SAX—whose principal scientists include Luigi Piro, Enrico Costa and John Heise—made it into space, on April 20, 1996.

Gamma-ray bursts were first discovered by accident, in the late 1960s, by the Vela series of spacecraft of the U.S. Department of Defense. These satellites were designed to ferret out the U.S.S.R.'s clandestine nuclear detonations in outer space—perhaps hidden behind the moon. Instead they came across spasms of radiation that did not originate from near Earth. In 1973 scientists concluded that a new astronomical phenomenon had been discovered.

These initial observations resulted in a flurry of speculation about the origins of gamma-ray bursts—involving black holes, supernovae or the dense, dark star remnants called neutron stars. There were, and still are, some critical unknowns. No one knew whether the bursts were coming from a mere 100 light-years away or a few billion. As a result, the energy of the original events could only be guessed at.

By the mid-1980s the consensus was that the bursts originated on nearby neutron stars in our galaxy. In particular, theorists were intrigued by dark lines in the spectra (component wavelengths spread out, as light is by a prism) of some bursts, which suggested the presence of intense magnetic fields. The gamma rays, they postulated, are emitted by electrons accelerated to relativistic speeds when magnetic field lines from a neutron star reconnect. A similar phenomenon on the sun—but at far lower energies—leads to flares.

In April 1991 the space shuttle *Atlantis* launched the Compton Gamma Ray Observatory, a satellite that carried the Burst And Transient Source Experiment (BATSE). Within a year BATSE had confounded all expectations. The distribution of gamma-ray bursts did not trace out the Milky Way, nor were the bursts associated with nearby galaxies or clusters of galaxies. Instead they were distributed isotropically, with any direction in the sky having roughly the same number. Theorists soon refined the galactic model: the bursts were now said to come from neutron stars in an extended spherical halo surrounding the galaxy.

One problem with this scenario is that Earth lies in the suburbs of the Milky Way, about 25,000 light-years from the core. For us to find ourselves near the center of a galactic halo, the latter must be truly enormous, almost 800,000 light-years in outer radius. If so, the halo of the neighboring Andromeda galaxy should be as extended and should start to appear in the distribution of gamma-ray bursts. But it does not.

This uniformity, combined with the data from GRB 970508, has convinced most astrophysicists that the bursts come from cosmological distances, on the order of three billion to 10 billion light-years away. At such a distance, though, the bursts

VERY LARGE ARRAY of radio telescopes (*right*) discovered radio waves from a burst (GRB 970508) for the first time in May 1997. The burst (*above, at center*) had a cosmological origin but showed no underlying galaxy, confounding theorists.

HUBBLE SPACE TELESCOPE

ROGER RESSMEYER *Corbis*

Gamma-Ray Bursts

should show the effects of the expansion of the universe. Galaxies that are very distant are moving away from Earth at great speeds; we know this because the light they emit shifts to lower, or redder, frequencies. Likewise, gamma-ray bursts should also show a "redshift," as well as an increase in duration.

Unfortunately, BATSE does not see, in the spectrum of gamma rays, bright or dark lines characterizing specific elements whose displacements would betray a shift to the red. (Nor does it detect the dark lines found by earlier satellites.) In April astronomers using the Keck II telescope in Hawaii obtained an optical spectrum of the afterglow of GRB 970228—smooth and red, with no telltale lines. Still, Jay Norris of the National Aeronautics and Space Administration Goddard Space Flight Center and Robert Mallozzi of the University of Alabama in Huntsville have statistically analyzed the observed bursts and report that the weakest, and therefore the most distant, show both a time dilation and a redshift. And the dark lines in the spectrum of GRB 970508 are substantially shifted to the red.

A Cosmic Catastrophe

One feature that makes it difficult to explain the bursts is their great variety. A burst may last from about 30 milliseconds to almost 1,000 seconds—and in one case, 1.6 hours. Some bursts show spasms of intense radiation, with no detectable emission in between, whereas others are smooth. Also complicated are the spectra—essentially, the colors of the radiation, invisible though they are. The bulk of a burst's energy is in radiation of between

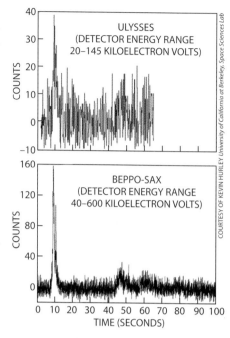

COURTESY OF KEVIN HURLEY University of California at Berkeley, Space Sciences Lab

TIME PROFILE of GRB 970228 taken by the Ulysses spacecraft (*top*) and by Beppo-SAX (*bottom*) shows a brief, brilliant flash of gamma rays.

100,000 and one million electron volts, implying an exceedingly hot source. (The photons of optical light, the primary radiation from the sun, have energies of a few electron volts.) Some bursts evolve smoothly to lower frequencies such as x-rays as time passes. Although this x-ray tail has less energy, it contains many photons.

If originating at cosmological distances, the bursts must have energies of perhaps 10^{52} ergs. (About 1,000 ergs can lift a gram by one centimeter.) This energy must be emitted within seconds or less from a tiny region of space, a few tens of kilometers across. It would seem we are dealing with a fireball.

The first challenge is to conceive of circumstances that would create a sufficiently energetic fireball. Most theorists favor a scenario in which a binary neutron-star system collapses [see "Binary Neutron Stars," by Tsvi Piran; SCIENTIFIC AMERICAN, May 1995]. Such a pair gives off gravitational energy in the form of radiation. Consequently, the stars spiral in toward each other and may ultimately merge to form a black hole. Theoretical models estimate that one such event occurs every 10,000 to one million years in a galaxy. There are about 10 billion galaxies in the volume of space that BATSE observes; that yields up to 1,000 bursts a year in the sky, a number that fits the observations.

Variations on this scenario involve a neutron star, an ordinary star or a white dwarf colliding with a black hole. The details of such mergers are a focus of intense study. Nevertheless, theorists agree that before two neutron stars,

X-RAY IMAGE taken by Beppo-SAX on February 28, 1997 (*left image*), localized GRB 970228 to within a few arc minutes, allowing ground-based telescopes to search for it. On March 3 the source was much fainter (*right image*).

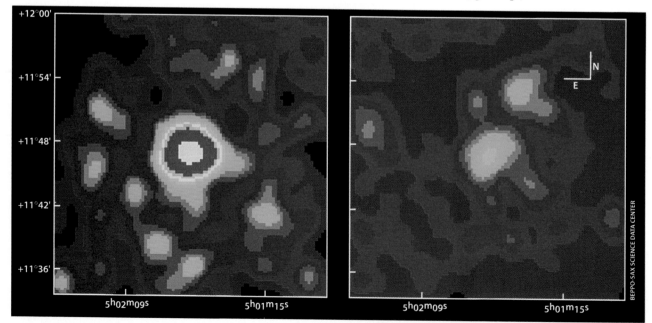

BEPPO-SAX SCIENCE DATA CENTER

Gamma-Ray Bursts

OPTICAL IMAGES of the region of GRB 970228 were taken by the William Herschel Telescope on the Canary Islands, on February 28 (*top*) and March 8 (*bottom*). A point of light in the first image has faded away in the second one, indicating a transient afterglow.

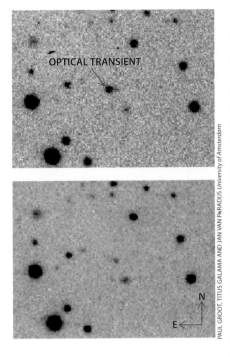

OPTICAL TRANSIENT

PAUL GROOT, TITUS GALAMA AND JAN VAN PARADIJS *University of Amsterdam*

say, collapse into a black hole, their death throes release as much as 10^{53} ergs. This energy emerges in the form of neutrinos and antineutrinos, which must somehow be converted into gamma rays. That requires a chain of events: neutrinos collide with antineutrinos to yield electrons and positrons, which then annihilate one another to yield photons. Unfortunately, this process is very inefficient, and recent simulations by Max Ruffert and Hans-Thomas Janka of the Max Planck Institute in Munich, as well as by other groups, suggest it may not yield enough photons.

Worse, if too many heavy particles such as protons are in the fireball, they reduce the energy of the gamma rays. Such proton pollution is to be expected, because the collision of two neutron stars must yield a potpourri of particles. But then all the energy ends up in the kinetic energy of the protons, leaving none for radiation. As a way out of this dilemma, Peter Mészáros of Pennsylvania State University and Martin J. Rees of the University of Cambridge have suggested that when the expanding fireball—essentially hot protons—hits surrounding gases, it produces a shock wave. Electrons accelerated by the intense electromagnetic fields in this wave then emit gamma rays.

A variation of this scenario involves internal shocks, which occur when different parts of the fireball hit one another at relativistic speeds, also generating gamma rays. Both the shock models imply that gamma-ray bursts should be followed by long afterglows of x-rays and visible light. In particular, Mario Vietri of the Astronomical Observatory of Rome has predicted detectable x-ray afterglows lasting for a month—and also noted that such afterglows do not occur in halo models. GRB 970228 provides the strongest evidence yet for such a tail.

There are other ways of generating the required gamma rays. Nir Shaviv and Arnon Dar of the Israel Institute of Technology in Haifa start with a fireball of unknown origin that is rich in heavy metals. Hot ions of iron or nickel could then interact with radiation from nearby stars to give off gamma rays. Simulations show that the time profiles of the resulting bursts are quite close to observations, but a fireball consisting entirely of heavy metals seems unrealistic.

Another popular mechanism invokes immensely powerful magnetic engines, similar to the dynamos that churn in the cores of galaxies. Theorists envision that instead of a fireball, a merger of two stars—of whatever kind—could yield a black hole surrounded by a thick, rotating disk of debris. Such a disk would be very short-lived, but the magnetic fields inside it would be astounding, some 10^{15} times those on Earth. Much as an ordinary dynamo does, the fields would extract rotational energy from the system, channeling it into two jets bursting out along the rotation axis.

The cores of these jets—the regions closest to the axis—would be free of proton pollution. Relativistic electrons inside them can then generate an intense, focused pulse of gamma rays. Although quite a few of the details remain to be worked out, many such scenarios ensure that mergers are the leading contenders for explaining bursts.

Still, gamma-ray bursts have been the subject of more than 3,000 papers—about one publication per recorded burst. Their transience has made them difficult to observe with a variety of instruments, and the resulting paucity of data has allowed for a proliferation of theories.

If one of the satellites detects a lensed burst, astronomers would have further confirmation that bursts occur at cosmological distances. Such an event might occur if an intervening galaxy or other massive object serves as a gravitational lens to bend the rays from a burst toward Earth. When optical light from a distant star is focused in this manner, it appears as multiple images of the original star, arranged in arcs around the lens. Gamma rays cannot be pinpointed with such accuracy; instead they are currently detected by instruments that have poor directional resolution.

Moreover, bursts are not steady sources like stars. A lensed gamma-ray burst would therefore show up as two bursts coming from roughly the same direction, having identical spectra and time profiles but different intensities and arrival times. The time difference would come from the rays' traversing curved paths of different lengths through the lens.

To further nail down the origins of the underlying explosion, we need data on other kinds of radiation that might

SPACE TELESCOPE SCIENCE INSTITUTE

SPACE TELESCOPE SCIENCE INSTITUTE

OPTICAL REMNANT of GRB 970228 was pictured by the Hubble Space Telescope. The afterglow (*near center of top image*), when seen in close-up (*bottom*), has a faint, elongated background glow that may correspond to a galaxy in which the burst occurred.

The Gamma-Ray Sky

Gamma-ray astronomy elucidates the structure and evolution of the universe by means of the photons of greatest energy. Because gamma rays are absorbed by the atmosphere of Earth and, moreover, are hard to detect, their study poses a challenge to technology.

Early detectors were flown on balloons. Nowadays instruments based in space survey the sky for these rays. The Compton Gamma Ray Observatory, launched in 1991, uses complex detectors to catch photons in the energy range of 10 kilo electron volts to 30 giga electron volts (GeV). Future instruments, such as the Gamma-ray Large Area Space Telescope (GLAST) planned for 2004, will survey the sky even more sensitively at higher energies of up to 300 GeV.

When a photon's energy becomes large enough, it creates an avalanche of particles on penetrating the atmosphere. These particles then emit optical light that can be detected on the ground by large mirrored collectors such as Whipple in Arizona. Whipple currently detects particles of energy 300 GeV or higher. If it is upgraded, as planned, to VERITAS (Very Energetic Radiation Imaging Telescope Array System), the array will detect particles of energy as low as 100 GeV, closing the gap with the satellite data.

Gamma rays are emitted by the most violent explosions in the universe. As a result, they allow astronomers to study essential processes such as the production of elements in the universe. Heavy elements created within stars are dispersed by supernovae explosions; new stars and planets are then born from the chemically enriched gas, ultimately incorporating the new substances into emerging life.

One of the nuclei thus produced and ejected is aluminum 26, which decays in about a million years by emitting a photon of 1.8 million eV (MeV). Two instruments on the Compton observatory map the sky in this line, thereby providing an image of the past supernovae activity in the Milky Way. Tens of thousands of supernovae (occurring at a rate of one per century) contribute to a diffuse glow at 1.8 MeV, providing testimony to the amazing cycle of stellar birth and death as an ongoing process. The INTEGRAL (International Gamma Ray Astrophysics Laboratory) satellite, to be launched early in the next century, will continue the quest for gamma-ray maps of special spectral lines, such as aluminum 26 and titanium 44.

On Compton, EGRET (Energetic Gamma Ray Experiment Telescope) has mapped the sky at energies above 100 MeV, finding a bright and diffuse glow concentrated along the galactic midplane. The radiation is emitted by fast particles—from supernovae explosions—as they slam into the molecular gas between the stars. Apart from tracing such remnants of violent processes, the EGRET image also shows pointlike sources. Some of these, close to the plane of the galaxy, are pulsars, stable cores left in the wake of supernovae.

These dense, compact objects often have extremely strong magnetic fields—a trillion times that of Earth—and rotate very rapidly, with periods of milliseconds. The magnetized atmospheres of some such "dead stars" emit strongly beamed gamma rays. But if the rays miss the detectors, astronomers may never notice the star even if it is nearby. Although radio astronomers have found about 1,000 pulsars, gamma-ray astronomers have detected only half a dozen. Even so, these gamma-ray pulsars have taught us a great deal about the behavior of matter under extreme conditions. One example is the process by which electrons emit radiation when in magnetic fields too high to be created on Earth.

Yet another kind of point source of gamma rays is a blazar. Blazars are active galaxies in whose centers lie black holes as massive as a billion suns. The gas and stars the black hole draws in emit a beam of gamma rays. These rays allow us to probe the conditions of matter near a black hole and the ways in which it spirals inward.

And then, of course, there are the gamma-ray bursters, perhaps the most mysterious of all.

—G.J.F. and D.H.H.

SKY MAP
(top) in photons of more than 100 million electron volts (MeV) traces the fastest particles in the universe, glowing when they interact with interstellar matter and light. The isolated spots far from the Milky Way (*lateral line*) are blazars. The map in photons of a precise energy, 1.8 MeV (*bottom*), reveals the presence of aluminum 26 and therefore the distribution of past supernovae. It demonstrates that the synthesis of elements and their dispersion from supernovae is an ongoing process throughout the galaxy.

EGRET, COMPTON OBSERVATORY (*top*); R. DIEHL AND U. OBERLACK *Max Planck Institute for Extraterrestrial Physics* AND COMPTEL, COMPTON OBSERVATORY (*bottom*)

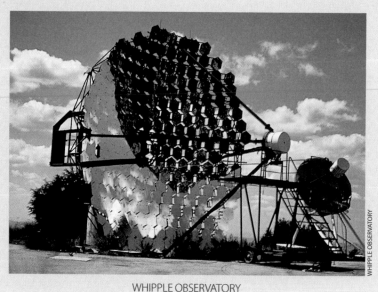

WHIPPLE OBSERVATORY

WHIPPLE OBSERVATORY
on Mount Hopkins in Arizona surveys the sky in gamma rays. An energetic gamma-ray photon penetrating the atmosphere releases a shower of optical photons that the 10-meter reflector detects.

Gamma-Ray Bursts

accompany a burst. Even better would be to identify the source. Until the observation of GRB 970228 such "counterparts" had proved exceedingly elusive. To find others, we must locate the bursts very precisely.

Since the early 1970s, Kevin Hurley of the University of California at Berkeley and Thomas Cline of the NASA Goddard Space Flight

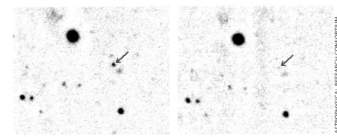

OPTICAL TRANSIENT for a third burst, GRB 971214, provided a New Year's gift to astronomers. The images were taken at the Apache Point Observatory in Sunspot, N.M., on December 15 (*left*) and 16 (*right*).

ASTROPHYSICAL RESEARCH CONSORTIUM

Center have worked to establish "interplanetary networks" of burst instruments. They try to put a gamma-ray detector on any spacecraft available or to send aloft dedicated devices. The motive is to derive a location to within arc minutes, by comparing the times at which a burst arrives at spacecraft separated by large distances.

From year to year, the network varies greatly in efficacy, depending on the number of participating instruments and their separation. At present, there are five components: BATSE, Beppo-SAX and the military satellite DMSP, all near Earth; Ulysses, far above the plane of the solar system; and the spacecraft Wind, orbiting the sun. The data from Beppo-SAX, Ulysses and Wind were used to triangulate GRB 970228. (BATSE was in Earth's shadow at the time.) The process, unfortunately, is slow—eight hours at best.

Watching and Waiting

Time is of the essence if we are to direct diverse detectors at a burst while it is glowing. Scott Barthelmy of the Universities Space Research Association at the NASA Goddard Space Flight Center has developed a system called GCN (Gamma-ray burst Coordinate Network) to transmit within seconds BATSE data on burst locations to ground-based telescopes.

BATSE consists of eight gamma-ray detectors pointing in different directions from eight corners of the Compton satellite; comparing the intensity of a burst at these detectors provides its location to roughly a few degrees but within several seconds. Often GCN can locate the burst even while it is in progress. The location is transmitted over the Internet to several dozen sites worldwide. In five more seconds, robotically controlled telescopes at Lawrence Livermore National Laboratory, among others, slew to the location for a look.

Unfortunately, only the fast-moving, smaller telescopes, which would miss a faint image, can contribute to the effort. The Livermore devices, for instance, could not have seen the afterglow of GRB 970228. Telescopes that are 100 times more sensitive are required. These mid-size telescopes would also need to be robotically controlled so they can slew very fast, and they must be capable of searching reasonably large regions. If they do find a transient afterglow, they will determine its location rather well, allowing much larger telescopes such as Hubble and Keck to look for a counterpart.

The long-lasting, afterglow following GRB 970228 gives new hope for this strategy. The HETE mission, directed by George Ricker of the Massachusetts Institute of Technology, is to be rebuilt and launched in about two years. It will survey the sky with x-ray detectors that can localize bursts to within several arc minutes. Ground-based optical telescopes will receive these locations instantly and start searching for transients.

Of course, we do not know what fraction of bursts exhibit a detectable afterglow. Moreover, even a field as small as arc minutes contains too many faint objects to make a search for counterparts easy.

To further constrain the models, we will need to look at radiation of both higher and lower frequency than that currently observed. The Compton satellite has seen a handful of bursts that emit radiation of up to 10 billion electron volts. Better data in this regime, from the Gamma-ray Large Area Space Telescope (GLAST), a satellite being developed by an international team of scientists, will greatly aid theorists. Photons of even higher energy—of about a trillion electron volts—might be captured by special ground-based gamma-ray telescopes. At the other end of the spectrum, soft x-rays, which have energies of up to roughly one kilo electron volt (keV), can help test models of bursts and obtain better fixes on position. In the range of 0.1 to 10 keV, there is a good chance of discovering absorption or emission lines that would tell volumes about the underlying fireball.

When the Hubble telescope was pointed to the location of GRB 970508, it picked up the fading light from the optical transient. Much to our surprise, however, it saw no galaxy in the immediate vicinity—not even a hint of one [*see left illustration on page 83*]. This absence emphasizes a potential problem noted by Bradley E. Schaefer of Yale University: bursts do not occur in the kind of bright galaxies within which one would expect an abundance of stars. So whereas astrophysicists now have strong evidence of the cosmological distances of bursts, we are still confounded as to their host environments and physical origins.

Just in time for New Year's 1998, nature provided a third afterglow from a gamma-ray burst. Again, Beppo-SAX discovered the initial event, following which Jules P. Halpern of Columbia University and John R. Thorstensen of Dartmouth College used the 2.4-meter telescope on Kitt Peak to find an optical transient. The glow dimmed in a manner similar to that of the previous two transients. As this article goes to press, we wait for Hubble to discern if this burst, GRB 971214, has a bright underlying galaxy or not. **SA**

The Authors

GERALD J. FISHMAN and DIETER H. HARTMANN bring complementary skills to the study of gamma-ray bursts. Fishman is an experimenter—the principal investigator for BATSE and a senior astrophysicist at the National Aeronautics and Space Administration Marshall Space Flight Center in Huntsville, Ala. He has received the NASA Medal for Exceptional Scientific Achievement three times and in 1994 was awarded the Bruno Rossi Prize of the American Astronomical Society. Hartmann is a theoretical astrophysicist at Clemson University in South Carolina; he obtained his Ph.D. in 1989 from the University of California, Santa Cruz. Apart from gamma-ray astronomy, his primary interests are the chemical dynamics and evolution of galaxies and stars. This article updates a version that appeared in *Scientific American* in July 1997.

For student exercises relating to this article, please see the back of this reader

Surveying Space-time with

*Exploding stars seen across immense distances
show that the cosmic expansion may be accelerating—
a sign that the universe may be driven apart
by an exotic new form of energy*

by Craig J. Hogan, Robert P. Kirshner and Nicholas B. Suntzeff

A long time ago (some five billion years), in a galaxy far, far away (about 2,000 megaparsecs), a long-dead star exploded with a flash brighter than a billion suns. Its light spread out across space, fading and stretching with the expanding cosmos, before some of it finally reached the earth. Within 10 minutes during one dark night in 1997, a few hundred photons from this supernova landed on the mirror of a telescope in Chile. A computer at the observatory then created a digital image that showed the arrival of this tiny blip of light. Though not very impressive to look at, for us this faint spot was a thrilling sight— a new beacon for surveying space and time.

We and our colleagues around the world have tracked the arrival of light from several dozen such supernovae and used these observations to map the overall shape of the universe and to chronicle its expansion. What we and another team of astronomers have recently discerned challenges decades of conventional wisdom: it seems the universe is bigger and emptier than suspected. Moreover, its ongoing expansion is not slowing down as much as many cosmologists had anticipated; in fact, it may be speeding up.

Star Warps

The history of cosmic expansion has been of keen interest for most of this century, because it reflects on both the geometry of the universe and the nature of its constituents—matter, light and possibly other, more subtle forms of energy. Albert Einstein's general theory of relativity knits together these fundamental properties of the universe and describes how they affect the motion of matter and the propagation of light, thereby offering predictions for concrete things that astronomers can actually measure.

Before the publication of Einstein's theory in 1916 and the first observations of cosmic expansion during the following decade, most scientists

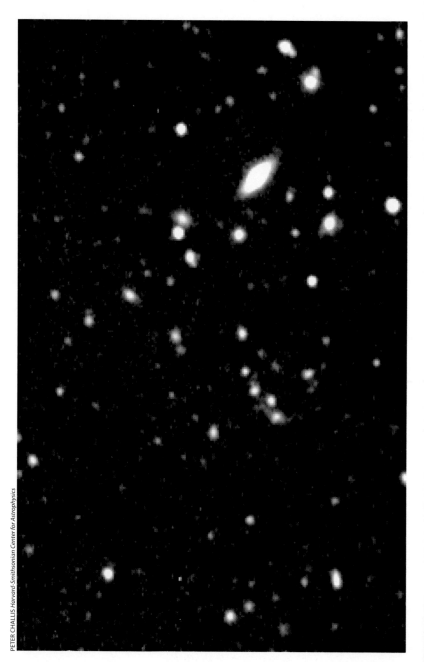

PETER CHALLIS *Harvard-Smithsonian Center for Astrophysics*

Supernovae

thought the universe stayed the same size. Indeed, Einstein himself distrusted his equations when he realized they implied a dynamic universe. But new measurements of galactic motions by Edwin P. Hubble and others left no doubt: faint, distant galaxies were flying away from the earth faster than bright, nearby ones, matching the predictions of general relativity for a universe that grows and carries galaxies farther apart. These researchers determined the outward velocities of galaxies from the shift of visible spectral lines to longer wavelengths (so-called redshifts). Though often ascribed to the Doppler effect—the phenomenon responsible for changing the pitch of a passing train whistle or car horn—the cosmological redshift is more correctly thought of as a result of the ongoing expansion of the universe, which stretches the wavelength of light passing between galaxies. Emissions from more distant objects, having traveled for a greater time, become more redshifted than radiation from nearer sources.

The technology of Hubble's day limited the initial probing of cosmic expansion to galaxies that were comparatively close. In the time it took light from these nearby galaxies to reach the earth, the universe had expanded by only a small fraction of its overall size. For such modest changes, redshift is directly proportional to distance; the fixed ratio of the two is called Hubble's constant and denotes the current rate of cosmic expansion. But astronomers have long expected that galaxies farther away would depart from this simple relation between redshift and distance, either because the pace of expansion has changed over time or because the intervening space is warped. Measuring this effect thus constitutes an important goal for cosmologists—but it is a difficult one, for it requires the means to determine the distances to galaxies situated tremendously far away.

WHERE'S THE SUPERNOVA? This pair of images, made by the authors' team using the four-meter-diameter Blanco Telescope at Cerro Tololo Inter-American Observatory in Chile, provided first evidence of one supernova. In the image at the right, obtained three weeks after the one at the left, the supernova visibly (but subtly) alters the appearance of one of the galaxies. Can you find it? Some differences are caused by varying atmospheric conditions. To check your identification, consult the key on the next page.

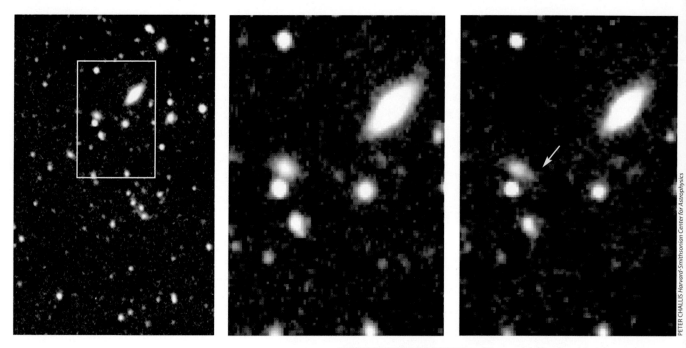

PETER CHALLIS *Harvard-Smithsonian Center for Astrophysics*

DISTANT SUPERNOVA, with a redshift of $z = 0.66$, appears by the arrow. The explosion of this star affects just a few picture elements in the image taken after the event.

Hubble and other pioneers estimated distances to various galaxies by assuming that they all had the same intrinsic brightness. According to their logic, ones that appeared bright were comparatively close and the ones that appeared dim were far away. But this methodology works only crudely, because galaxies differ in their properties. And it fails entirely for distant sources whose light takes so long to reach the earth that it reveals the faraway galaxies as they were billions of years ago (that is, in their youth), because their intrinsic brightness could have been quite different from that of more mature galaxies seen closer to home. It is difficult to disentangle these evolutionary changes from the effects of the expansion, so astronomers have long sought other "standard candles" whose intrinsic brightness is better known.

To be visible billions of light-years away, these beacons must be very bright. During the early 1970s, some cosmic surveyors tried using quasars, which are immensely energetic sources (probably powered by black holes swallowing stars and gas). But the quasars they studied proved even more diverse than galaxies and thus were of little use.

About the same time, other astronomers began exploring the idea of using supernovae—exploding stars—as standard candles for cosmological studies. That approach was controversial because supernovae, too, show wide variation in their properties. But in the past decade research by members of our team has enabled scientists to determine the intrinsic brightness of one kind of supernova—type Ia—quite precisely.

Death Star

What is a type Ia supernova? Essentially, it is the blast that occurs when a dead star becomes a natural thermonuclear bomb. Spectacular as this final transformation is, the progenitor begins its life as an ordinary star, a stable ball of gas whose outer layers are held up by heat from steady nuclear reactions in its core, which convert hydrogen to helium, carbon, oxygen, neon and other elements. When the star dies, the nuclear ashes coalesce into a glowing ember, compressed by gravity to the size of the earth and a million times the density of ordinary matter.

Most such white dwarf stars simply cool and fade away, dying with a whimper. But if one is orbiting near another star, it can slurp up material from its companion and become denser and denser until a runaway thermonuclear firestorm ignites. The nuclear cataclysm blows the dwarf star completely apart, spewing out material at about 10,000 kilometers per second. The glow of this expanding fireball takes about three weeks to reach its maximum brightness and then declines over a period of months.

These supernovae vary slightly in their brilliance, but there is a pattern: bigger, brighter explosions last somewhat longer than fainter ones. So by monitoring how long they last, astronomers can correct for the differences and deduce their inherent brightness to within 12 percent. Over the past decade studies of nearby type Ia supernovae with modern detectors have made these flashes the best calibrated standard candles known to astronomers.

One of these candles lights up somewhere in a typical galaxy about once every 300 years. Although such stellar explosions in our own Milky Way are rare celestial events, if you monitor a few thousand other galaxies, you can expect that about one type Ia supernova will appear every month. Indeed, there are so many galaxies in the universe that, somewhere in the sky, supernovae bright enough to study erupt every few seconds. All astronomers have to do is find them and study them carefully. For the past few years, that effort has occupied both our research group, dubbed the "High-Z Team" (for the letter that astronomers use to denote redshift), a loose affiliation organized in 1995 by Brian P. Schmidt of Mount Stromlo and Siding Spring Observatories in Australia, and a competing collaboration called the Supernova Cosmology Project, which began in 1988 and is led by Saul Perlmutter of Lawrence Berkeley National Laboratory.

Although the two teams have independent programs, they are exploiting the same fundamental advance: the deployment of large electronic light detectors on giant telescopes, a combination that produces digital images of faint objects over sizable swaths of the sky. A prime example of this new technology (one

Surveying Space-time with Supernovae

that has served both teams) is the Big Throughput Camera, which was developed by Gary M. Bernstein of the University of Michigan and J. Anthony Tyson of Lucent Technologies. When this camera is placed at the focus of the four-meter Blanco Telescope at Cerro Tololo Inter-American Observatory in Chile, a single exposure covers an area about as big as the full moon and creates a picture of about 5,000 galaxies in 10 minutes.

Finding distant supernovae is just a matter of taking images of the same part of the sky a few weeks apart and searching for changes that might be exploding stars. Because the digital light detectors can count the number of photons in each picture element precisely, we simply subtract the first image from the second and look for significant differences from zero. Because we are checking thousands of galaxies in each image pair, we can be confident that the search of multiple pairs will find many supernovae—as long as the weather is good. Fortunately, the location of the observatory, in the foothills of the Andes on the southern fringe of Chile's Atacama Desert (one of the driest places in the world), usually provides clear skies. Betting that we will make some good discoveries, we schedule observing time in advance on a battery of other telescopes around the world so that follow-up measurements can start before the supernovae fade away.

In practice, the search for exploding stars in the heavens whips up its own burst of activity on the ground, because we must acquire and compare hundreds of large, digital images at a breakneck pace. We commandeer computers scattered throughout the Cerro Tololo observatory for the tasks of aligning the images, correcting for differences in atmospheric transparency and image size, and subtracting the two scans. If all goes well, most of the galaxies disappear, leaving just a little visual "noise" in the difference of the two images. Larger

signals indicate some new or changing object, such as variable stars, quasars, asteroids—and in a few cases, supernovae.

Our software records the position of new objects and attempts to identify which are truly supernovae. But the automated tests are imperfect, and we must scrutinize the images by eye to decide whether a putative supernova is real. Because we must immediately pursue our discoveries with other telescopes, the analysis must be done quickly. During these exhausting times, the observatory becomes a sweatshop of astronomers and visiting students, who work around the clock for days at a stretch, sustained by enthusiasm and Chilean pizza.

We next target the best supernova candidates with the largest optical instruments in the world, the recently constructed Keck telescopes in Hawaii. These critical observations establish whether or not the objects discovered are in fact type Ia supernovae, gauge their intrinsic brightness more exactly and determine their redshifts.

On the Dark Side

Others in our group, working with telescopes in Australia, Chile and the U.S., also follow these supernovae to track how their brilliance peaks and then slowly fades. The observing campaign for a single supernova spans months, and the final analysis often has to wait a year or more, when the light of the exploded star has all but disappeared, so we can obtain a good image of its host galaxy. We use this final view to subtract the constant glow of the galaxy from the images of the supernova. Our best measurements come from the Hubble Space Telescope, which captures such fine details that the exploding star stands out distinctly from its host galaxy.

The two teams have now studied a total of a few score high-

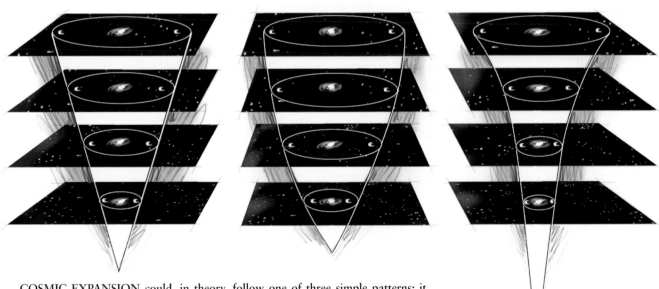

COSMIC EXPANSION could, in theory, follow one of three simple patterns: it may be constant (*left*), decelerating (*center*) or accelerating (*right*). In each case, a given portion of the universe grows in size as time passes (*from bottom to top*). But the age of the universe—the time elapsed since the beginning of the expansion—is greater for an accelerating universe and less for a decelerating universe, compared with the constant expansion case.

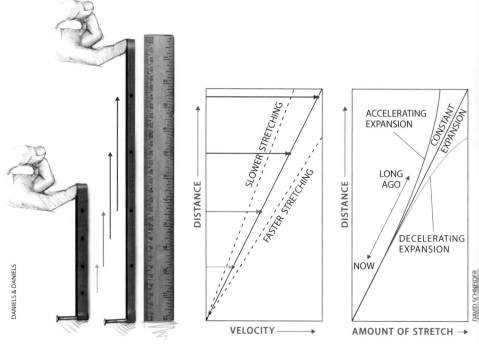

RUBBER BAND EXPERIMENT shows the linear relation between recession velocity and distance. Here two snapshots are shown of a rubber band pulled upward at a certain rate. The velocity of different points marked on the band is given by the length of the colored arrows. For example, the point closest to the origin moves the least during the interval between snapshots, so its velocity is the smallest (*yellow arrow*). In contrast, the farthest point moves the most, so its velocity is the highest (*violet arrow*). The slope of the resulting line is the rate of expansion (*left graph*). If the rate changes over time, the slope, too, will change (*right graph*). Earlier times plot toward the upper right, because light from more distant objects takes longer to reach the earth, the origin of the plot. If the rate was slower in the past—indicating that the expansion has been accelerating—the line will curve upward (*red line*). If the rate was faster—as in a decelerating expansion—it will curve downward (*blue line*).

DANIELS & DANIELS

DAVID SCHNEIDER

redshift supernovae, ones that erupted between four and seven billion years ago, when the universe was between one half and two thirds of its present age. Both groups were hit with a major surprise: the supernovae are fainter than expected. The difference is slight, the distant supernovae being, on average, only 25 percent dimmer than forecast. But this result is enough to call long-standing cosmological theories into question.

Before drawing any sweeping conclusions, astronomers on both teams have been asking themselves whether there is a prosaic explanation for the relative dimness of these distant supernovae. One culprit could be murkiness caused by cosmic dust, which might screen out some of the light. We think we can discount this possibility, however, because dust grains would tend to filter out blue light more than red, causing the supernovae to appear redder than they really are (in the same way that atmospheric dust colors the setting sun). We observe no such alteration. Also, we would expect that cosmic dust, unless it is spread very smoothly throughout space, would introduce a large amount of variation in the measurements, which we do not see either.

Another possible disturbance is gravitational lensing, the bending of light rays as they skirt galaxies en route. Such lensing occasionally causes brightening, but most often it causes demagnification and thus can contribute to the dimness of distant supernovae. Yet calculations show that this effect becomes important only for sources located even farther away than the supernovae we are studying, so we can dismiss this complication as well.

Finally, we worried that the distant supernovae are somehow different from the nearby ones, perhaps forming from younger stars that contain fewer heavy elements than is typical in more mature galaxies. Although we cannot rule out this possibility, our analysis already tries to take such differences into account. These adjustments appear to work well when we apply them to nearby galaxies, which range widely in age, makeup and the kinds of supernovae seen.

Because none of these mundane effects fits the new observa-

tions, we and many other scientists are now led to think that the unexpected faintness of distant supernovae is indeed caused by the structure of the cosmos. Two different properties of space and of time might be contributing.

First, space might have negative curvature. Such warping is easier to comprehend with a two-dimensional analogy. Creatures living in a perfectly flat, two-dimensional world (like the characters in Edwin A. Abbott's classic novel *Flatland*) would find that a circle of radius r has a circumference of exactly $2\pi r$. But if their world were subtly bent into a saddle shape, it would have a slight negative curvature [see "Inflation in a Low-Density Universe," by Martin A. Bucher and David N. Spergel, on page 62]. The two-dimensional residents of Saddleland might be oblivious to this curvature until they measured a large circle of some set radius and discovered that its circumference was greater than $2\pi r$.

Most cosmologists have assumed, for various theoretical reasons, that our three-dimensional space, like Flatland, is not curved. But if it had negative curvature, the large sphere of radiation given off by an ancient supernova would have a greater area than it does in geometrically flat space, making the source appear strangely faint.

A second explanation for the unexpected dimness of distant supernovae is that they are farther away than their redshifts suggest. Viewed another way, supernovae located at these enormous distances seem to have less redshift than anticipated. To account for the smaller redshift, cosmologists postulate that the universe must have expanded more slowly in the past than they had expected, giving less of an overall stretch to the universe and to the light traveling within it.

The Force

What is the significance of the cosmic expansion slowing less quickly than previously thought? If the universe is made of normal matter, gravity must steadily slow the expansion. Little slowing, as indicated by the supernovae measure-

Surveying Space-time with Supernovae

ments, thus implies that the overall density of matter in the universe is low.

Although this conclusion undermines theoretical preconceptions, it agrees with several other lines of evidence. For example, astronomers have noted that certain stars appear to be older than the accepted age of the universe—a clear impossibility. But if the cosmos expanded more slowly in the past, as the supernovae now indicate, the age of the universe must be revised upward, which may resolve the conundrum. The new results also accord with other recent attempts to ascertain the total amount of matter, such as studies of galaxy clusters [see "The Evolution of Galaxy Clusters," by J. Patrick Henry, Ulrich G. Briel and Hans Böhringer; SCIENTIFIC AMERICAN, December 1998].

What does the new understanding of the density of matter in the universe say about its curvature? According to the principles of general relativity, curvature and deceleration are connected. To paraphrase John A. Wheeler, formerly at Princeton University: matter tells space-time how to curve, and space-time tells matter how to move. A small density of matter implies negative curvature as well as little slowing. If the universe is nearly empty, these two dimming effects are both near their theoretical maximum.

The big surprise is that the supernovae we see are fainter than predicted even for a nearly empty universe (which has maximum negative curvature). Taken at face value, our observations appear to require that expansion is actually accelerating with time. A universe composed only of normal matter cannot grow in this fashion, because its gravity is always attractive. Yet according to Einstein's theory, the expansion can speed up if an exotic form of energy fills empty space everywhere. This strange "vacuum energy" is embodied in Einstein's equations as the so-called cosmological constant. Unlike ordinary forms of mass and energy, the vacuum energy adds gravity that is repulsive and can drive the universe apart at ever increasing speeds [see "Cosmological Antigravity," by Lawrence M. Krauss, on page 94]. Once we admit this extraordinary possibility, we can explain our observations perfectly, even assuming the flat geometry beloved of theorists.

Evidence for a strange form of energy imparting a repulsive gravitational force is the most interesting result we could have hoped for, yet it is so astonishing that we and others remain suitably skeptical. Fortunately, advances in the technology available to astronomers, such as new infrared detectors and the Next Generation Space Telescope, will soon permit us to test our conclusions by offering greater precision and reliability. These marvelous instruments will also allow us to perceive even fainter beacons that flared still longer ago in galaxies that are much, much farther away. [SA]

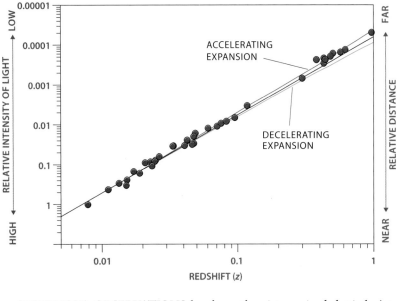

DAVID SCHNEIDER; SOURCE: CRAIG J. HOGAN, ROBERT P. KIRSHNER AND NICHOLAS B. SUNTZEFF

SUPERNOVA OBSERVATIONS by the authors' team (*red dots*) deviate slightly but significantly from the pattern that many theoreticians expected—namely, a fairly rapid deceleration (*blue line*) that should occur if the universe is "flat" and has no cosmological constant. These observations indicate that the universe has only 20 percent of the matter necessary to make it flat, because it is decelerating more slowly than predicted (*black line*). The measurements even suggest that expansion is accelerating, perhaps because of a nonzero cosmological constant (*red line*).

The Authors

CRAIG J. HOGAN, ROBERT P. KIRSHNER and NICHOLAS B. SUNTZEFF share a longstanding interest in big things that go bang. Hogan earned his doctorate at the University of Cambridge and is now a professor and chair of the astronomy department at the University of Washington. Kirshner attained his Ph.D. at the California Institute of Technology, studying a type Ia supernova observed in 1972 (the brightest one seen since 1937). He is a professor of astronomy at Harvard University and also serves as an associate director of the Harvard-Smithsonian Center for Astrophysics. Suntzeff received his Ph.D. at the University of California, Santa Cruz. He works at Cerro Tololo Inter-American Observatory in La Serena, Chile, and is made of elements formed in supernovae over five billion years ago.

Further Reading

THE LITTLE BOOK OF THE BIG BANG. Craig J. Hogan. Springer-Verlag, 1998.
DISCOVERY OF A SUPERNOVA EXPLOSION AT HALF THE AGE OF THE UNIVERSE. S. Perlmutter, G. Aldering, M. Della Valle, S. Deustua, R. S. Ellis, S. Fabbro, A. Fruchter, G. Goldhaber, D. E. Groom, I. M. Hook, A. G. Kim, M. Y. Kim, R. A. Knop, C. Lidman, R. G. McMahon, Peter Nugent, R. Pain, N. Panagia, C. R. Pennypacker, P. Ruiz-Lapuente, B. Schaefer and N. Walton (The Supernova Cosmology Project) in *Nature*, Vol. 391, pages 51–54; January 1, 1998. Preprint available at xxx.lanl.gov/abs/astro-ph/9712212 on the World Wide Web.
OBSERVATIONAL EVIDENCE FROM SUPERNOVAE FOR AN ACCELERATING UNIVERSE AND A COSMOLOGICAL CONSTANT. Adam G. Riess, Alexei V. Filippenko, Peter Challis, Alejandro Clocchiattia, Alan Diercks, Peter M. Garnavich, Ron L. Gilliland, Craig J. Hogan, Saurabh Jha, Robert P. Kirshner, B. Leibundgut, M. M. Phillips, David Reiss, Brian P. Schmidt, Robert A. Schommer, R. Chris Smith, J. Spyromilio, Christopher Stubbs, Nicholas B. Suntzeff and John Tonry in *Astronomical Journal*, Vol. 116, No. 3, pages 1009–1038; September 1998. Preprint at xxx.lanl.gov/abs/astro-ph/9805201 on the World Wide Web. Additional information on supernova searches is available at cfa-www.harvard.edu/cfa/oir/Research/supernova/HighZ.html and www-supernova.lbl.gov/ on the World Wide Web.

For student exercises relating to this article, please see the back of this reader

Cosmological Antigravity

The long-derided cosmological constant—a contrivance of Albert Einstein's that represents a bizarre form of energy inherent in space itself—is one of two contenders for explaining changes in the expansion rate of the universe

by Lawrence M. Krauss

Novelist and social critic George Orwell wrote in 1946, "To see what is in front of one's nose requires a constant struggle." These words aptly describe the workings of modern cosmology. The universe is all around us—we are part of it—yet scientists must sometimes look halfway across it to understand the processes that led to our existence on the earth. And although researchers believe that the underlying principles of nature are simple, unraveling them is another matter. The clues in the sky can be subtle. Orwell's adage is doubly true for cosmologists grappling with the recent observations of exploding stars hundreds of millions of light-years away. Contrary to most expectations, they are finding that the expansion of the universe may not be slowing down but rather speeding up.

Astronomers have known that the visible universe is expanding since at least 1929, when Edwin P. Hubble demonstrated that distant galaxies are moving apart as they would if the entire cosmos were uniformly swelling in size. These outward motions are counteracted by the collective gravity of galaxy clusters and all the planets, stars, gas and dust they contain. Even the minuscule gravitational pull of, say, a paper clip retards cosmic expansion by a slight amount. A decade ago a congruence of theory and observations suggested that there were enough paper clips and other matter in the universe to almost, but never quite, halt the expansion. In the geometric terms that Albert Einstein encour-

SO-CALLED EMPTY SPACE is actually filled with elementary particles that pop in and out of existence too quickly to be detected directly. Their presence is the consequence of a basic principle of quantum mechanics combined with special relativity: nothing is exact, not even nothingness. The aggregate energy represented by these "virtual" particles, like other forms of energy, could exert a gravitational force, which could be either attractive or repulsive depending on physical principles that are not yet understood. On macroscopic scales the energy could act as the cosmological constant proposed by Albert Einstein.

Types of Matter

Type	Likely Composition	Main Evidence	Approximate Contribution to Ω
Visible matter	Ordinary matter (composed mainly of protons and neutrons) that forms stars, dust and gas	Telescope observations	0.01
Baryonic dark matter	Ordinary matter that is too dim to see, perhaps brown or black dwarfs (massive compact halo objects, or MACHOs)	Big bang nucleosynthesis calculations and observed deuterium abundance	0.05
Nonbaryonic dark matter	Exotic particles such as "axions," neutrinos with mass or weakly interacting massive particles (WIMPs)	Gravity of visible matter is insufficient to account for orbital speeds of stars within galaxies and of galaxies within clusters	0.3
Cosmological "dark matter"	Cosmological constant (energy of empty space)	Microwave background suggests cosmos is flat, but there is not enough baryonic or nonbaryonic matter to make it so	0.6

CONTENTS OF THE UNIVERSE include billions and billions of galaxies, each one containing an equally mind-boggling number of stars. Yet the bulk seems to consist of "dark matter" whose identity is still uncertain. The cosmological constant, if its existence is confirmed, would act like a yet more exotic form of dark matter on cosmological scales. The quantity omega, Ω, is the ratio of the density of matter or energy to the density required for flatness.

aged cosmologists to adopt, the universe seemed to be "flat."

The flat universe is an intermediate between two other plausible geometries, called "open" and "closed." In a cosmos where matter does battle with the outward impulse from the big bang, the open case represents the victory of expansion: the universe would go on expanding forever. In the closed case, gravity would have the upper hand, and the universe would eventually collapse again, ending in a fiery "big crunch." The open, closed and flat scenarios are analogous to launching a rocket faster than, slower than or exactly at the earth's escape velocity—the speed necessary to overcome the planet's gravitational attraction.

LETTER FROM EINSTEIN, then at the Prussian Academy of Sciences in Berlin, to German mathematician Hermann Weyl concedes that a universe of unchanging size would be prone to expansion or collapse: "In the De Sitter universe two fluid and unstable distinct points separate at an accelerated pace. If there is no quasi-static world, then away with the cosmological term!"

That we live in a flat universe, the perfect balance of power, is one of the hallmark predictions of standard inflationary theory, which postulates a very early period of rapid expansion to reconcile several paradoxes in the conventional formulation of the big bang. Although the visible contents of the cosmos are clearly not enough to make the universe flat, celestial dynamics indicate that there is far more matter than meets the eye. Most of the material in galaxies and assemblages of galaxies must be invisible to telescopes. Over a decade ago I applied the term "quintessence" to this so-called dark matter, borrowing a term Aristotle used for the ether—the invisible material supposed to permeate all of space [see "Dark Matter in the Universe," by Lawrence M. Krauss; SCIENTIFIC AMERICAN, December 1986].

Yet an overwhelming body of evidence now implies that even the unseen matter is not enough to produce a flat universe. Perhaps the universe is not flat but rather open, in which case scientists must modify—or discard—inflationary theory [see "Inflation in a Low-Density Universe," by Martin A. Bucher and David N. Spergel, on page 62]. Or maybe the universe really is flat. If that is so, its main constituents cannot be visible matter, dark matter or radiation. Instead the universe must be composed largely of an even more ethereal form of energy that inhabits empty space, including that which is in front of our noses.

Fatal Attraction

The idea of such energy has a long and checkered history, which began when Einstein completed his general theory of relativity, more than a decade before Hubble's convincing demonstration that the universe is expanding. By tying together space, time and matter, relativity promised what had previously been impossible: a scientific understanding not merely of the dynamics of objects within the universe but of the universe itself. There was only one problem. Unlike other fundamental forces felt by matter, gravity is universally attractive—it only pulls; it cannot push. The unrelenting gravitational attraction of matter could cause the universe to collapse eventually. So Einstein, who presumed the universe to be static and stable, added an extra term to his equations, a "cosmological term," which could stabilize the universe by producing a new long-range force throughout space. If its value were positive, the term would represent a repulsive force—a kind of antigravity that could hold the universe up under its own weight.

Alas, within five years Einstein abandoned this kludge, which he associated with his "biggest blunder." The stability offered by the term turned out to be illusory, and, more important, evidence had begun to mount that the universe is expanding. As early as 1923, Einstein wrote in a letter to mathematician Hermann Weyl that "if there is no quasi-static world, then away with the cosmological term!" Like the ether before it, the term appeared to be headed for the dustbin of history.

Physicists were happy to do without such an intrusion. In the general theory of relativity, the source of gravitational forces (whether attractive or repulsive) is energy. Matter is simply one form of energy. But Einstein's cosmological term is distinct. The energy associated with it does not depend on position or time—hence the name "cosmological constant." The force caused by the constant operates even in the complete absence of matter or radiation. Therefore, its source must be a curious energy that resides in empty space. The cosmological constant, like the ether, endows the void with an almost metaphysical aura. With its demise, nature was once again reasonable.

Or was it? In the 1930s glimmers of the cosmological constant arose in a completely independent context: the effort to combine the laws of quantum mechanics with Einstein's special theory of relativity. Physicists Paul A. M. Dirac and later Richard Feynman, Julian S. Schwinger and Shinichiro Tomonaga showed that empty space was more complicated than anyone had previously imagined. Elementary particles, it turned out, can spontaneously pop out of nothingness and disappear again, if they do so for a time so short that one cannot measure them directly [see "Exploiting Zero-Point Energy," by Philip Yam; SCIENTIFIC AMERICAN, December 1997]. Such virtual particles, as they are called, may appear as far-fetched as angels sitting on the head of a pin. But there is a difference. The unseen particles produce measurable effects, such as alterations to the energy levels of atoms as well as forces between nearby metal plates. The theory of virtual particles agrees with observations to nine decimal places. (Angels, in contrast, normally have no discernible effect on either atoms or plates.) Like it or not, empty space is not empty after all.

Virtual Reality

If virtual particles can change the properties of atoms, might they also affect the expansion of the universe? In 1967 Russian astrophysicist Yakov B. Zeldovich showed that the energy of virtual particles should act precisely as the energy associated with a cosmological constant. But there was a serious problem. Quantum theory predicts a whole spectrum of virtual particles, spanning every possible wavelength. When physicists add up all the effects, the total energy comes out infinite. Even if theorists ignore quantum effects smaller than a certain wavelength—for which poorly understood quantum gravitational effects presumably alter things—the calculated vacuum energy is roughly 120 orders of magnitude larger than the energy contained in all the matter in the universe.

What would be the effect of such a humongous cosmological constant? Taking a cue from Orwell's maxim, you can easily put an observational limit on its value. Hold out your hand and look at your fingers. If the constant were as large as

quantum theory naively suggests, the space between your eyes and your hand would expand so rapidly that the light from your hand would never reach your eyes. To see what is in front of your face would be a constant struggle (so to speak), and you would always lose. The fact that you can see anything at all means that the energy of empty space cannot be large. And the fact that we can see not only to the ends of our arms but also to the far reaches of the universe puts an even more stringent limit on the cosmological constant: almost 120 orders of magnitude smaller than the estimate mentioned above. The discrepancy between theory and observation is the most perplexing quantitative puzzle in physics today [see "The Mystery of the Cosmological Constant," by Larry Abbott; SCIENTIFIC AMERICAN, May 1988].

The simplest conclusion is that some as yet undiscovered physical law causes the cosmological constant to vanish. But as much as theorists might like the constant to go away, various astronomical observations—of the age of the universe, the density of matter and the nature of cosmic structures—all independently suggest that it may be here to stay.

Determining the age of the universe is one of the long-standing issues of modern cosmology. By measuring the velocities of galaxies, astronomers can calculate how long it took them to arrive at their present positions, assuming they all started out at the same place. For a first approximation, one can ignore the deceleration caused by gravity. Then the universe would expand at a constant speed and the time interval would just be the ratio of the distance between galaxies to their measured speed of separation—that is, the reciprocal of the famous Hubble constant. The higher the value of the Hubble constant, the faster the expansion rate and hence the younger the universe.

Hubble's first estimate of his eponymous constant was almost 500 kilometers per second per megaparsec—which would mean that two galaxies separated by a distance of one megaparsec (about three million light-years) are moving apart, on average, at 500 kilometers per second. This value would imply a cosmic age of about two billion years, which is in painful contradiction with the known age of the earth—about four billion years. When the gravitational attraction of matter is taken into account,

DEMONSTRATION OF CASIMIR EFFECT is one way that physicists have corroborated the theory that space is filled with fleeting "virtual particles." The Casimir effect generates forces between metal objects—for instance, an attractive force between parallel metal plates (*above*). Loosely speaking, the finite spacing of the plates prevents virtual particles larger than a certain wavelength from materializing in the gap. Therefore, there are more particles outside the plates than between them, an imbalance that pushes the plates together (*right*). The Casimir effect has a distinctive dependence on the shape of the plates, which allows physicists to tease it out from other forces of nature.

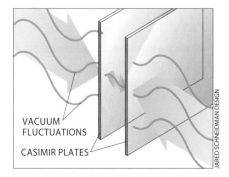

VACUUM
FLUCTUATIONS

CASIMIR PLATES

the analysis predicts that objects moved faster early on, taking even less time to get to their present positions than if their speed had been constant. This refinement reduces the age estimate by one third, unfortunately worsening the discrepancy.

Over the past seven decades, astronomers have improved their determination of the expansion rate, but the tension between the calculated age of the universe and the age of objects within it has persisted. In the past decade, with the launch of the Hubble Space Telescope and the development of new observational techniques, disparate measurements of the Hubble constant are finally beginning to converge. Wendy L. Freedman of the Carnegie Observatories and her colleagues have inferred a value of 73 kilometers per second per megaparsec (with a most likely range, depending on experimental error, of 65 to 81) [see "The Expansion Rate and Size of the Universe," by Wendy L. Freedman; SCIENTIFIC AMERICAN, November 1992]. These results put the upper limit on the age of a flat universe at about 10 billion years.

The Age Crisis

Is that value old enough? It depends on the age of the oldest objects that astronomers can date. Among the most ancient stars in our galaxy are those found in tight groups known as globular clusters, some of which are located in the outskirts of our galaxy and are thus thought to have formed before the rest of the Milky Way. Estimates of their age, based on calculations of how fast stars burn their nuclear fuel, traditionally ranged from 15 to 20 billion years. Such objects appeared to be older than the universe.

To determine whether this age conflict was the fault of cosmology or of stellar modeling, in 1995 my colleagues—Brian C. Chaboyer, then at the Canadian Institute of Theoretical Astrophysics, Pierre Demarque of Yale University and Peter J. Kernan of Case Western Reserve University—and I reassessed the globular cluster ages. We simulated the life cycles of three million different stars whose properties spanned the existing uncertainties, and then compared our model stars with those in globular clusters. The oldest, we concluded, could be as young as 12.5 billion years old, which was still at odds with the age of a flat, matter-dominated universe.

But two years ago the Hipparcos satellite, launched by the European Space Agency to measure the locations of over 100,000 nearby stars, revised the distances to these stars and, indirectly, to globular clusters. The new distances affected estimates of their brightness and forced us to redo our analysis, because brightness determines the rate at which stars consume fuel and hence their life spans. Now it seems that globulars could, at the limit of the observational error bars, be as young as 10 billion years old, which is just consistent with the cosmological ages.

But this marginal agreement is uncomfortable, because it requires that both sets of age estimates be near the edge of their allowed ranges. The only thing left that can give is the assumption that we live in a flat, matter-dominated universe. A lower density of matter, signifying an open universe with slower deceleration, would ease the tension somewhat. Even so, the only way to lift the age above 12.5 billion years would be to consider a universe dominated not by matter but by a cosmological constant. The resulting repulsive force would cause the Hubble expansion to accelerate over time. Galaxies would have been moving apart slower than they are today, taking longer to reach their present separation, so the universe would be older.

The current estimates of age are merely suggestive. Meanwhile other pillars of observational cosmology have recently been shaken, too. As astronomers have surveyed ever larger regions of the cosmos, their ability to tally up its contents has improved. Now the case is compelling that the total amount of matter is insufficient to yield a flat universe.

This cosmic census first involves calculations of the synthesis of elements by the big bang. The light elements in the cosmos—hydrogen and helium and their rarer isotopes, such as deuterium—were created in the early universe in relative amounts that depended on the number of available protons and neutrons, the constituents of normal matter. Thus, by comparing the abundances of the various isotopes, astronomers can deduce the total amount of ordinary matter that was produced in the big bang. (There could, of course, also be other matter not composed of protons and neutrons.)

The relevant observations took a big step forward in 1996 when David R. Tytler and Scott Burles of the University of California at San Diego and their colleagues measured the primordial abundance of deuterium using absorption of quasar light by intergalactic hydrogen clouds. Because these clouds have never contained stars, their deuterium could only have been created by the big bang. Tytler and Burles's finding implies that the average density of ordinary matter is between 4 and 7 percent of the amount needed for the universe to be flat.

Astronomers have also probed the density of matter by studying the largest gravitationally bound objects in the universe: clusters of galaxies. These groupings of hundreds of galaxies account for almost all visible matter. Most of their luminous content takes the form of hot intergalactic gas, which emits x-rays. The temperature of this gas, inferred from the spectrum of the x-rays, depends on the total mass of the cluster: in more massive clusters, the gravity is stronger and hence the pressure that supports the gas against gravity must be larger, which drives the temperature higher. In 1993 Simon D. M. White, now at the Max Planck Institute for Astrophysics in Garching, Germany, and his colleagues compiled information about several different clusters to argue that luminous matter accounted for between 10 and 20 percent of the total mass of the objects. When combined with the measurements of deuterium, these results imply that the total density of clustered matter including protons and neutrons as well as

Summary of Inferred Values of Cosmic Matter Density

Observation	Ω_{matter}
Age of universe	<1
Density of protons and neutrons	0.3–0.6
Galaxy clustering	0.3–0.5
Galaxy evolution	0.3–0.5
Cosmic microwave background radiation	≲1
Supernovae type Ia	0.2–0.5

MEASUREMENTS of the contribution to Ω from matter are in rough concordance. Although each measurement has its skeptics, most astronomers now accept that matter alone cannot make Ω equal to 1. But other forms of energy, such as the cosmological constant, may also pitch in.

Cosmological Antigravity

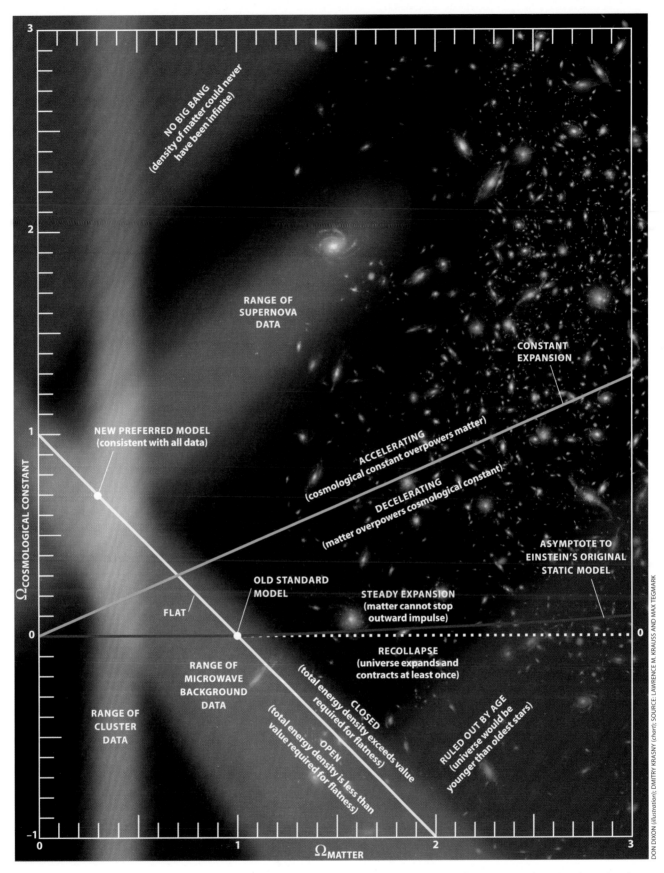

Vertical axis label: $\Omega_{\text{COSMOLOGICAL CONSTANT}}$

Horizontal axis label: Ω_{MATTER}

NO BIG BANG
(density of matter could never have been infinite)

RANGE OF
SUPERNOVA
DATA

CONSTANT
EXPANSION

NEW PREFERRED MODEL
(consistent with all data)

ACCELERATING
(cosmological constant overpowers matter)

DECELERATING
(matter overpowers cosmological constant)

ASYMPTOTE TO
EINSTEIN'S ORIGINAL
STATIC MODEL

OLD STANDARD
MODEL

STEADY EXPANSION
(matter cannot stop
outward impulse)

FLAT

RANGE OF
MICROWAVE
BACKGROUND
DATA

RECOLLAPSE
(universe expands and
contracts at least once)

RANGE OF
CLUSTER
DATA

CLOSED
(total energy density exceeds value
required for flatness)

OPEN
(total energy density is less than
value required for flatness)

RULED OUT BY AGE
(universe would be
younger than oldest stars)

DON DIXON (*illustration*); DMITRY KRASNY (*chart*); SOURCE: LAWRENCE M. KRAUSS AND MAX TEGMARK

MAP OF MODELS shows how the unfolding of the universe depends on two key cosmological quantities: the average density of matter (*horizontal axis*) and the density of energy in the cosmological constant (*vertical axis*). Their values, given here in standard cosmological units, have three distinct effects. First, their sum (which represents the total cosmic energy content) determines the geometry of space-time (*yellow line*). Second, their difference (which represents the relative strength of expansion and gravity) determines how the expansion rate changes over time (*blue line*). These two effects have been probed by recent observations (*shaded regions*). The third, a balance of the two densities, determines the fate of the universe (*red line*). The three effects have many permutations—unlike the view of cosmology in which the cosmological constant is assumed to be zero and there are only two possible outcomes.

Average Density of the Universe

COSMIC COINCIDENCE is one of many mysteries swirling about the cosmological constant. The average density of ordinary matter decreases as the universe expands (*red*). The equivalent density represented by the cosmological constant is fixed (*black*). So why, despite these opposite behaviors, do the two have nearly the same value today? The consonance is either happenstance, a precondition for human existence (an appeal to the weak anthropic principle) or an indication of a mechanism not currently envisaged.

GEORGE MUSSER AND DMITRY KRASNY

The Fate of the Universe

The cosmological constant changes the usual simple picture of the future of the universe. Traditionally, cosmology has predicted two possible outcomes that depend on the geometry of the universe or, equivalently, on the average density of matter. If the density of a matter-filled universe exceeds a certain critical value, it is "closed," in which case it will eventually stop expanding, start contracting and ultimately vanish in a fiery apocalypse. If the density is less than the critical value, the universe is "open" and will expand forever. A "flat" universe, for which the density equals the critical value, also will expand forever but at an ever slower rate.

Yet these scenarios assume that the cosmological constant equals zero. If not, it—rather than matter—may control the ultimate fate of the universe. The reason is that the constant, by definition, represents a fixed density of energy in space. Matter cannot compete: a doubling in radius dilutes its density eightfold. In an expanding universe the energy density associated with a cosmological constant must win out. If the constant has a positive value, it generates a long-range repulsive force in space, and the universe will continue to expand even if the total energy density in matter and in space exceeds the critical value. (Large negative values of the constant are ruled out because the resulting attractive force would already have brought the universe to an end.)

Even this new prediction for eternal expansion assumes that the constant is indeed constant, as general relativity suggests that it should be. If in fact the energy density of empty space does vary with time, the fate of the universe will depend on how it does so. And there may be a precedent for such changes—namely, the inflationary expansion in the primordial universe. Perhaps the universe is just now entering a new era of inflation, one that may eventually come to an end. —*L.M.K.*

more exotic particles such as certain dark-matter candidates—is at most 60 percent of that required to flatten the universe.

A third set of observations, ones that also bear on the distribution of matter at the largest scales, supports the view that the universe has too little mass to make it flat. Perhaps no other subfield of cosmology has advanced so much in the past 20 years as the understanding of the origin and nature of cosmic structures. Astronomers had long assumed that galaxies coalesced from slight concentrations of matter in the early universe, but no one knew what would have produced such undulations. The development of the inflationary theory in the 1980s provided the first plausible mechanism—namely, the enlargement of quantum fluctuations to macroscopic size.

Numerical simulations of the growth of structures following inflation have shown that if dark matter was not made from protons and neutrons but from some other type of particle (such as so-called WIMPs), tiny ripples in the cosmic microwave background radiation could grow into the structures now seen. Moreover, concentrations of matter should still be evolving into clusters of galaxies if the overall density of matter is high. The relatively slow growth of the number of rich clusters over the recent history of the universe suggests that the density of matter is less than 50 percent of that required for a flat universe [see "The Evolution of Galaxy Clusters," by J. Patrick Henry, Ulrich G. Briel and Hans Böhringer; SCIENTIFIC AMERICAN, December 1998].

Nothing Matters

These many findings that the universe has too little matter to make it flat have become convincing enough to overcome the strong theoretical prejudice against this possibility. Two interpretations are viable: either the universe is open, or it is made flat by some additional form of energy that is not associated with ordinary matter. To distinguish

Cosmological Antigravity

between these alternatives, astronomers have been pushing to measure the microwave background at high resolution. Initial indications now favor a flat universe. Meanwhile researchers studying distant supernovae have provided the first direct, if tentative, evidence that the expansion of the universe is accelerating, a telltale sign of a cosmological constant with the same value implied by the other data [see "Surveying Space-time with Supernovae," by Craig J. Hogan, Robert P. Kirshner and Nicholas B. Suntzeff, on page 46]. Observations of the microwave background and of supernovae illuminate two different aspects of cosmology. The microwave background reveals the geometry of the universe, which is sensitive to the total density of energy, in whatever form, whereas the supernovae directly probe the expansion rate of the universe, which depends on the difference between the density of matter (which slows the expansion) and the cosmological constant (which can speed it up).

Together all these results suggest that the constant contributes between 40 and 70 percent of the energy needed to make the universe flat [see illustration on page 99]. Despite the preponderance of evidence, it is worth remembering the old saw that an astronomical theory whose predictions agree with all observations is probably wrong, if only because some of the measurements or some of the predictions are likely to be erroneous. Nevertheless, theorists are already scrambling to understand what 20 years ago would have been unthinkable: a cosmological constant greater than zero yet much smaller than current quantum theories predict. Some feat of fine-tuning must subtract virtual-particle energies to 123 decimal places but leave the 124th untouched—a precision seen nowhere else in nature.

One direction, explored recently by Steven Weinberg of the University of Texas at Austin and his colleagues, invokes the last resort of cosmologists, the anthropic principle. If the observed universe is merely one of an infinity of disconnected universes—each of which might have slightly different constants of nature, as suggested by some incarnations of inflationary theory combined with emerging ideas of quantum gravity—then physicists can hope to estimate the magnitude of the cosmological constant by asking in which universes intelligent life is likely to evolve. Weinberg and others have arrived at a result that is compatible with the apparent magnitude of the cosmological constant today.

Most theorists, however, do not find these notions convincing, as they imply that there is no reason for the constant to take on a particular value; it just does. Although that argument may turn out to be true, physicists have not yet exhausted the other possibilities, which might allow the constant to be constrained by fundamental theory rather than by accidents of history [see "The Anthropic Principle," by George Gale; SCIENTIFIC AMERICAN, December 1981].

Another direction of research follows in a tradition established by Dirac. He argued that there is one measured large number in the universe—its age (or, equivalently, its size). If certain physical quantities were changing over time, they might naturally be either very large or very small today [see "P. A. M. Dirac and the Beauty of Physics," by R. Corby Hovis and Helge Kragh; SCIENTIFIC AMERICAN, May 1993]. The cosmological constant could be one example. It might not, in fact, be constant. After all, if the cosmological constant is fixed and nonzero, we are living at the first and only time in the cosmic history when the density of matter, which decreases as the universe expands, is comparable to the energy stored in empty space. Why the coincidence? Several groups have instead imagined that some form of cosmic energy mimics a cosmological constant but varies with time.

This concept was explored by P. James E. Peebles and Bharat V. Ratra of Princeton University a decade ago. Motivated by the new supernova findings, other groups have resurrected the idea. Some have drawn on emerging concepts from string theory. Robert Caldwell and Paul J. Steinhardt of the University of Pennsylvania have reproposed the term "quintessence" to describe this variable energy. It is one measure of the theoretical conundrum that the dark matter that originally deserved this term now seems almost mundane by comparison. As much as I like the word, none of the theoretical ideas for this quintessence seems compelling. Each is ad hoc. The enormity of the cosmological-constant problem remains.

How will cosmologists know for certain whether they have to reconcile themselves to this theoretically perplexing universe? New measurements of the microwave background, the continued analysis of distant supernovae and measurements of gravitational lensing of distant quasars should be able to pin down the cosmological constant over the next few years. One thing is already certain. The standard cosmology of the 1980s, postulating a flat universe dominated by matter, is dead. The universe is either open or filled with an energy of unknown origin. Although I believe the evidence points in favor of the latter, either scenario will require a dramatic new understanding of physics. Put another way, "nothing" could not possibly be more interesting. ⬛

The Author

LAWRENCE M. KRAUSS works at the interface of physics and astronomy. He studies the workings of stars, black holes, gravitational lenses and the early universe in order to shed light on particle physics beyond the current Standard Model, including the unification of forces, quantum gravity and explanations for dark matter. Krauss is currently chair of the physics department at Case Western Reserve University. He is the author of four popular books, most recently *Beyond Star Trek*, which looks at the science depicted in movies and on television.

Further Reading

DREAMS OF A FINAL THEORY. Steven Weinberg. Pantheon Books, 1992.
PRINCIPLES OF PHYSICAL COSMOLOGY. P. James E. Peebles. Princeton University Press, 1993.
BEFORE THE BEGINNING: OUR UNIVERSE AND OTHERS. Martin Rees. Addison-Wesley, 1997.
THE AGE OF GLOBULAR CLUSTERS IN LIGHT OF HIPPARCOS: RESOLVING THE AGE PROBLEM? Brian Chaboyer, Pierre Demarque, Peter J. Kernan and Lawrence M. Krauss in *Astrophysical Journal*, Vol. 494, No. 1, pages 96–110; February 10, 1998. Preprint available at http://xxx.lanl.gov/abs/astro-ph/9706128 on the World Wide Web.
THE END OF THE AGE PROBLEM, AND THE CASE FOR A COSMOLOGICAL CONSTANT REVISITED. Lawrence M. Krauss in *Astrophysical Journal*, Vol. 501, No. 2, pages 461–466; July 10, 1998. Preprint available at xxx.lanl.gov/abs/astro-ph/9706227 on the World Wide Web.
LIVING WITH LAMBDA. J. D. Cohn. Preprint available at xxx.lanl.gov/abs/astro-ph/9807128 on the World Wide Web.

For student exercises relating to this article, please see the back of this reader

Cosmological Antigravity

SCIENTIFIC AMERICAN   January 1999   101

Searching for Life in Other Solar Systems

Life remains a phenomenon we know only on Earth.
But an innovative telescope in space could change that by detecting
signs of life on planets orbiting other stars

by Roger Angel and Neville J. Woolf

The search for extraterrestrial life can now be extended to planets outside our solar system. After years of looking, astronomers have turned up evidence of giant planets orbiting several distant stars similar to our sun. Smaller planets around these and other stars may have evolved living organisms. Finding extraterrestrial life may seem a Herculean task, but a space telescope mission called the Terrestrial Planet Finder, which the National Aeronautics and Space Administration plans to start in 2005, aims to locate such planets and search for evidence of life-forms, such as the primitive ones on Earth.

The largest and most powerful telescope now in space, the Hubble Space Telescope, can just make out mountains on Mars at 30 kilometers (19 miles). Pictures sharp enough to display geologic features of planets around other stars would require an array of space telescopes the size of the U.S. But pictures of Earth do not reveal the presence of life unless they are taken at very high resolution. Such images could be obtained with unmanned spacecraft sent to other solar systems, but the huge distance between Earth and any other planet makes this approach impractical.

Taking photographs, however, is not the best way to study distant planets. Spectroscopy, the technique astronomers use to obtain information about stars, can also reveal much about planets. In spectroscopy, light originating from an object in space is analyzed for unique markers that help researchers piece together characteristics such as the celestial body's temperature, atmospheric pressure and chemical composition. Simple life-forms on our planet have profoundly altered conditions on Earth in ways that a distant observer could perceive by spectroscopy of the planet atmosphere.

Fossil records indicate that within a billion years of Earth's formation, as soon as heavy bombardment by asteroids ceased, primitive organisms such as bacteria and algae evolved and spread around the globe. These organisms represented the totality of life here for the next two billion years; consequently, if life exists on other planets, it might well be in this highly uncommunicative form.

Earth's humble blue-green algae do not operate radio transmitters. Yet they are chemical engineers, honed by evolution, operating on a huge scale. As algae became more widespread, they began adding large quantities of oxygen to the atmosphere. The production of oxygen, fueled by energy derived

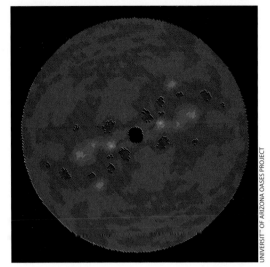

IMAGE OF DISTANT PLANETS, created from simulated interferometer signals, indicates what astronomers might reasonably expect to see with a space-based telescope. This study displays a system about 30 light-years away, with four planets roughly equivalent in luminosity to Earth. (Each planet appears twice, mirrored across the star.) With this sensitivity, the authors speculate that the instrument could easily examine the planet found in 1996 orbiting 47 Ursae Majoris.

UNIVERSITY OF ARIZONA OASES PROJECT

from sunlight, is fundamental to carbon-based life: the simplest organisms take in water, nitrogen and carbon dioxide as nutrients and then release oxygen into the atmosphere as waste. Oxygen is a chemically reactive gas; without continued replenishment by algae and, later in Earth's evolution, by plants, its concentration would fall. Thus, the presence of large amounts of oxygen in a planet's atmosphere is a good indicator that some form of carbon-based life may exist there.

In 1993 the Galileo space probe detected oxygen's distinctive spectrum in the red region of visible light from Earth. Indeed, this observation tells us that for a billion years—since plant and animal life has flourished on Earth—a signal of life's presence has radiated into space. The clincher that reveals life processes are occurring on Earth is the simultaneous presence in the planet's spectrum of methane, which is unstable around oxygen but which life continuously replenishes.

What constitutes detection of distant life? Some scientists hold that because life elsewhere is improbable, proof of its detection requires strong evidence. It seems likely, though, that life on other planets would have a carbon-based chemistry similar to our own. Carbon is particularly suitable as a building block of life: it is abundant in the universe, and no other known element can form the myriad of complex but stable molecules necessary for life as we know it. We believe that if a planet looks like Earth and has liquid water and oxygen (evident as ozone), then this would present strong evidence for its having life. If such a planet were found, subsequent investigations could strengthen the case by searching for the more elusive spectral observation of methane.

Of course, there could be some nonbiological oxygen source on a lifeless planet, a possibility that must be considered. Conversely, life could arise from some other type of chemistry that does not generate oxygen. Yet we still should be able to detect any stirrings from chemical residues.

Searching for Another Earth

Planets similar to Earth in size and distance from their sun—ones likely to have oceans of water—represent the most plausible homes for carbon-based life in other solar systems. Water provides a solvent for life's biochemical reactions and serves as a source of needed hydrogen. If each star has planets spanning a range of orbital distances, as occurs in our solar system, then one of those planets is likely to orbit at the right distance to sustain liquid water—even if the star shines more or less brightly than the sun.

Temperature, though, means little if a planet's gravitational pull cannot hold on to oceans and an atmosphere. If distance from a star were the only factor to consider, Earth's moon would have liquid water. But gravity depends on the size and density of the body. Because the moon is smaller and less

SPACE-BASED TELESCOPE SYSTEM
that can search for life-bearing planets has been proposed by the authors. The instrument, a type of interferometer, could be assembled at the proposed international space station (lower left). Subsequently, electric propulsion would send the 50- to 75-meter-long device into an orbit around the sun roughly the same as Jupiter's. Such a mission is at the focus of the National Aeronautics and Space Administration's plans to study neighboring planetary systems.

dense than Earth, its gravitational pull is much weaker. Any water or layers of atmosphere that might develop on or around such a body would quickly be lost to space.

Clearly, we need a technique to reveal characteristics as specific as what chemicals can be found on a planet. Previously we mentioned that the visible radiation coming from a planet can confirm the presence of certain molecules, in particular oxygen, that are known to support life. But distinguishing faint oxygen signals in light reflected by a small planet orbiting even a nearby star is extraordinarily difficult.

A larger version of the Hubble Space Telescope, specially equipped for extremely accurate optical correction, possibly could spot Earth-like planets if they are orbiting the three nearest sunlike stars and search them spectroscopically for oxygen. A more robust method for sampling dozens of stars is needed.

Faced with this quandary, in 1986 we proposed, along with Andrew Y. S. Cheng, now at the University of Hong Kong, that midinfrared wavelengths would serve as the best spectral region in which to find planets and to search for extraterrestrial life. This type of radiation—really the planet's radiated heat—has a wavelength 10 to 20 times longer than that of visible light. At these wavelengths, a planet emits about 40 times as many photons—particles of light—as it does at shorter wavelengths. The nearby star would outshine the planet "only" 10 million times, a ratio 1,000 times more favorable than that which red light offers.

Moreover, three key compounds that we would expect to find on inhabited planets—ozone (a form of oxygen usually located high in the atmosphere), carbon dioxide and water—leave strong imprints in a planet's infrared spectrum. Once again, our solar system provides promising support for this technique: a survey of the infrared emissions of local planets reveals that only Earth displays the infrared signature of life. Although Earth, Mars and Venus all have atmospheres with carbon dioxide, only Earth shows the signature of plentiful water and ozone. Sensitively indicating oxygen, ozone would have appeared on Earth a billion years before oxygen's infrared spectral feature grew detectable.

What kind of telescope do we need to locate Earth-like planets and pick up their infrared emissions? Some of today's ground-based telescopes can detect strong infrared radiation emanating from stars. But the telescope's own heat plus atmospheric absorptions would swamp any sign of a planet. Obviously, we reasoned, we must move the telescope into space.

Even then, to distinguish a planet's radiation from that of its star, a traditional telescope must be much larger than any ground-based or orbiting telescope built to date. Because light cannot be focused to a spot smaller than its wavelength, even a perfect telescope cannot form ideal images. At best, light will focus to a fuzzy core surrounded by a faint halo. If the halo surrounding the star extends beyond the planet's orbit, then we cannot discern the much dimmer body of the planet inside it. By making a telescope mirror and the resulting image very large, we can, in principle, make the image of a star as sharp as desired.

Because we can predict a telescope's performance, we know in advance what kind of image quality to expect. For example, to monitor the infrared spectrum of an Earth-like planet circling, say, a star 30 light-years away, we need a supergiant space telescope, close to 60 meters in diameter. We have made recent steps toward the technology for such telescopes, but 60 meters remains far beyond reach.

Rethinking the Telescope

We knew that to develop a more compact telescope to locate small, perhaps habitable, planets would require some tricks. Twenty-three years ago Ronald N. Bracewell of Stanford University suggested a good strategy when he showed how two small telescopes could together search for large, cool planets similar to Jupiter. Bracewell's proposed instrument consisted of two one-meter telescopes separated by 20 meters. Each telescope alone yields blurred pictures, yet together the two could discern distant worlds.

With both telescopes focused on the same star, Bracewell saw that he could invert light waves from one telescope (flipping peaks into troughs), then merge that inverted light with light from the second telescope. With precisely overlapping im-

Building an Earth-Based Interferometer

A consortium of American, Italian and German astronomers is now building a ground-based interferometer on Mount Graham in Arizona. At the Mirror Lab on the University of Arizona campus, where one of us (Angel) works, technicians have cast the first of two 8.4-meter-diameter mirrors (right), the largest ever made. Mounted side by side in the Large Binocular Telescope, two such mirrors will serve as a Bracewell interferometer, measuring heat emitted around nearby stars potentially hosting Earth-like planets.

Deformable secondary mirrors will correct for atmospheric blurring. This system is sensitive enough to detect giant planets and dust clouds around stars but not enough to spot another Earth-like planet. Designing a superior space-based interferometer depends on critical dust measurements. If dust clouds around other stars prove much denser than the cloud around the sun, then placing a Terrestrial Planet Finder instrument far from the sun (to avoid local heat from interplanetary dust) will offer no advantage. Instead an interferometer with larger mirrors that is closer to Earth will be needed.
—R.A. and N.J.W.

GIANT MIRROR at the University of Arizona
is to be mounted in the Large Binocular Telescope.

ages, the star's light—from its core and surrounding halo—would cancel out. Yet the planet's signal, which emanates from a slightly different direction, would remain intact. Scientists refer to this type of instrument as an interferometer because it reveals details about a light source by employing interference of light waves.

Bracewell's envisioned telescope would have enough sensitivity to spot Jupiter-size planets, although Earth-size planets would still be too faint to detect. To see Earth-size planets, an interferometer must cancel starlight more completely. In 1990, however, one of us (Angel) showed that such precision becomes possible if more than two telescopes are involved.

Another problem—even after canceling starlight completely—stems from background heat radiated from our solar system's cloud of dust particles, referred to as the zodiacal glow. As Bracewell realized, this glow would nearly overwhelm the signal of a giant planet, let alone that of an Earth-size one. Alain Léger and his collaborators at the University of Paris proposed the practical solution of placing the device in orbit around the sun, at roughly Jupiter's distance, where the dust is so cold that its background thermal radiation is negligible. He showed that an orbiting interferometer at that distance with telescopes as small as one meter in diameter would be sensitive enough to detect an Earth-size planet. Only if the star under study has its own thick dust cloud would detection be obscured, a difficulty that can be assessed with ground-based observations [see box on opposite page].

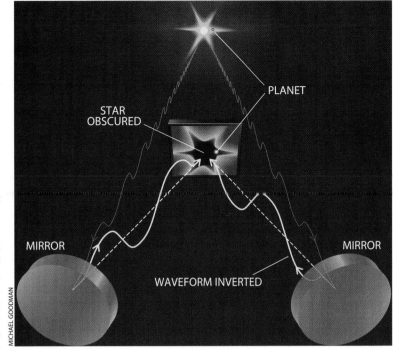

CANCELING STARLIGHT enables astronomers to see dim planets typically obscured by stellar radiance. Two telescopes focused on the same star (top) can cancel out much of its light: one telescope inverts the light—making peaks into troughs and vice versa (right). When the inverted light is combined with the noninverted starlight from the second telescope (left), the light waves interfere with one another, and the image of the star then vanishes (center).

Space-Based Interferometer

In 1995 NASA selected three teams to investigate various methods for discovering planets around other stars. We assembled an international team that included Bracewell, Léger and his colleague Jean-Marie Mariotti of the Paris Observatory, as well as some 20 other scientists and engineers. The two of us at the University of Arizona studied the potential of a new approach, an interferometer with two pairs of mirrors all arranged in a straight line.

Because this interferometer cancels starlight very effectively, it could span about 75 meters, a size offering important advantages. It permits astronomers to reconstruct actual images of planets orbiting a star, as well as to observe stars over a wide range of distances without expanding or contracting the device. As we envision the orbiting interferometer, it could point to a different star every day while returning to interesting systems for more observations.

If pointed at our own solar system from a nearby star, the interferometer could pick out Venus, Earth, Mars, Jupiter and Saturn. Its data could be analyzed to find the chemical composition of each planet's atmosphere. The device could easily study the newly discovered planet around 47 Ursae Majoris. More important, this interferometer could identify Earth-like planets that otherwise elude us, checking such planets for the presence of carbon dioxide, water and ozone—perhaps even methane.

Thanks to new ultralightweight mirrors developed for

NASA's Next Generation Space Telescope, a space-based interferometer combining telescopes as large as six meters in diameter looks feasible. Such an interferometer would suffer less from background heat and would function effectively in a near-Earth orbit. Also, it could better handle emissions from dust clouds around nearby candidate stars, if these clouds prove denser than those around the sun.

Building the interferometer would be a substantial undertaking, perhaps an international project, and many of the details have yet to be worked out. NASA has challenged designers of the Terrestrial Planet Finder to keep construction and launch costs below $500 million. A first industrial analysis indicates the price tag is not unrealistic.

The discovery of life on another planet may arguably be the crowning achievement of the exploration of space. Finding life elsewhere, NASA administrator Daniel S. Goldin has said, "would change everything—no human endeavor or thought would be unchanged by that discovery." SA

The Authors

ROGER ANGEL and NEVILLE J. WOOLF have collaborated for 15 years on methods for making better telescopes. They are based at Steward Observatory at the University of Arizona. A fellow of the Royal Society, Angel directs the Steward Observatory Mirror Laboratory. Woolf has pioneered techniques to minimize the distortion of images caused by the atmosphere. Angel and Woolf consider the quest for distant planets to be the ultimate test for telescope builders; they are meeting this challenge by pushing the limits of outer-space observation technology, such as adaptive optics and space telescopes. This article updates a version that appeared in Scientific American in April 1996.

For student exercises relating to this article, please see the back of this reader

MICHAEL GOODMAN

Exercises

Questions for "Robots vs. Humans: Who Should Explore Space?" by Francis Slakey and Paul D. Spudis
(PAGES 2-7)

1. Spudis is a geologist, and Slakey is a physicist. Discuss how the differences in their backgrounds could explain why one of them supports the human exploration of space and the other opposes it.

2. (a) Using the figures given by Slakey in the article, calculate the cost per kilogram of placing a payload in Earth orbit using the space shuttle. Assume that the shuttle carries its maximum amount of payload and delivers it all to orbit. (b) From 1995 to 1999, the space shuttle flew an average of six times per year. What was the cost per year to each person in the United States (population 275 million)? Compare that cost to the annual U.S. expenditure of about $24 per person per year on weapons that, according to the U.S. military, are neither needed nor wanted.

3. The unmanned Mars Pathfinder mission landed a 360-kilogram spacecraft on the Martian surface on July 4, 1997. (a) Using the cost of this mission as given by Slakey, estimate the cost of transporting 1 kilogram of material from Earth to Mars. (b) A manned mission to Mars might require transporting 50,000 kilograms of material (including the mass of the crew and their provisions for a three-year round-trip) to that planet. Estimate the cost of such a mission. (c) After reading Slakey's and Spudis's discussions, would you oppose or support such a manned mission? Explain your reasoning.

4. (a) Find the distance (in kilometers) from Earth to Mars when the two planets are closest, that is, when Mars is at opposition (see Figure 4-6 on page 77 of Universe). For simplicity, make the approximation that the orbits of Earth and Mars are circular, and that the radii of the orbits are given by the semimajor axes listed in Appendix 1 on page 759 of Universe. Give your answer in kilometers. (b) Using the same approximation as in (a), find the distance (in kilometers) from Earth to Mars when the two planets are farthest apart, i.e. when Mars is at conjunction (see Figure 4-6 on page 77 of Universe). (c) Radio waves travel at the speed of light, 3×10^5 km/s. Find the time required for a radio signal to go from the Earth to Mars and back to Earth under the circumstances in (a) and (b). Give your answers in minutes. (d) Use your answers to (c) to explain why it is difficult for an operator on Earth to control a robot spacecraft on Mars, as described by Spudis in the article.

5. Use the data given by Slakey in the article to determine the orbital period of the International Space Station. Use Newton's form of Kepler's third law, described in Box 4-2 on page 84 and in Section 4-7 of Universe, and assume that the orbit is circular. The mass of the station is so small compared to Earth's mass that it can be ignored. The mass and diameter of the Earth are given in Appendices 1 and 2 on page 759 of Universe. Give your answer in minutes. (Hint: Slakey gives the altitude of the station above the Earth's surface. The radius of the circular orbit is the distance from the station to the center of the Earth.)

Questions for "Migrating Planets" by Renu Malhotra
(PAGES 8-15)

1. (a) Malhotra describes how Pluto's orbit is in 3:2 resonance with Neptune's orbit. If there was a planet with an orbit in 3:2 resonance with Jupiter's orbit, what would be that planet's semimajor axis? (Hint: See Table 7-1 on page 164 of Universe.) (b) Is there a planet whose semimajor axis is in 3:2 resonance with Jupiter? What does this suggest about the stability of an orbit in 3:2 resonance with Jupiter's as compared to an orbit in 3:2 resonance with Neptune's?

2. If you throw a baseball so that it hits a second, stationary baseball, the second ball will recoil with about the same speed as the first ball had before the collision. But if you hit the stationary baseball with a fast-moving bat (which has much more mass than the ball), the baseball will fly off moving much faster than the bat. Use this observation to explain why Jupiter was the most effective of all the planets at ejecting planetesimals from the early solar system.

3. According to Malhotra's calculations, the five outer planets of the solar system were originally at different distances from the Sun than they are today. Which were originally closer to the Sun, and which were originally farther away?

4. The four inner planets are thought not to have undergone the same sort of "planetary migration" as the five outer planets. Suggest why not.

5. Several planets have been discovered orbiting other stars (see Section 7-9 of Universe). Most of these planets are comparable to or more massive than Jupiter but are in much smaller orbits than Jupiter's. Give at least two reasons why many astronomers think that these planets formed in larger orbits around their stars, then migrated inward.

Questions for "Global Climate Change on Venus" by Mark A. Bullock and David H. Grinspoon
(PAGES 16-23)

1. Define the following terms used in the article (a dictionary will be useful for some terms): (a) mélange; (b) lineament; (c) tesserae; (d) biota; (e) anthropogenic.

2. (a) The age of Venus, and of the solar system as a whole, is thought to be about 4.6 billion (4.6×10^9) years. Calculate the number of impact craters that should have been formed on the surface of Venus in the history of the planet. Use the rate of crater formation given in the article. (b) How does your answer to (a) compare to the number of craters actually observed on Venus, as given in the article? (Two such craters are shown in Figures 11-18 and 11-19 on page 275 of Universe.) Where on Venus are craters observed? What do these facts tell us about the geologic history of Venus?

3. How are water vapor (H_2O) and sulfur dioxide (SO_2) added to the atmosphere of Venus? Do they remain in the atmosphere? If not, where do they go? How are these gases thought to have affected the planet's surface temperature over the past 800 million years?

4. What geologic evidence on Venus indicates that the planet once had a much hotter surface than today?

5. Describe how the absence of water on Venus helps explain the lack of plate tectonic activity on that planet.

Questions for "The Mars Pathfinder Mission" by Matthew P. Golombek
(PAGES 24-31)

1. Although the rocks at the Mars Pathfinder landing site have been exposed for billions of years, they show relatively little erosion. Explain why.

2. How does the surface texture of the rocks seen by the Mars Pathfinder suggest that they are of volcanic origin?

3. Describe three geologic features discovered by the Mars Pathfinder that suggest that Mars once had abundant water.

4. How does the soil found at the Mars Pathfinder site compare to that found at the sites of the two Viking Landers? What does this imply about the origin of this soil?

5. Mars Pathfinder had no seismological experiments on board. Nonetheless, scientists were able to use data from Mars Pathfinder to learn about the internal structure of Mars. Explain how this was done.

Questions for "The Hidden Ocean of Europa" by Robert T. Pappalardo, James W. Head and Ronald Greeley
(PAGES 32-41)

1. Are there any places on Europa where Jupiter can never be seen? Explain.

2. What is the evidence that the dark, wedge-shaped bands on Europa are regions where the surface has pulled completely apart?

3. Why are there only a few impact craters on Europa? What does the shape of the craters tell us about the ice layer that covers Europa?

4. What is the evidence that the material beneath Europa's surface is probably not pure water?

5. Explain how a spacecraft in orbit around Europa could determine whether there is liquid water beneath Europa's surface.

Questions for "The Oort Cloud" by Paul R. Weissman
(PAGES 42-47)

1. What are Jupiter-family comets? Explain why these comets are thought to come from the Kuiper belt (see Section 17-8 of Universe) rather than the Oort cloud.

2. According to the article, about one-third of the long-period comets have orbital periods of one million (10^6) years or more. (a) Calculate the semimajor axis (in AU) of the orbit of a comet with a million-year period. (Hint: See Section 4-4 and Box 4-2 on page 84 of Universe.) (b) If such a comet passes very close to the Sun at perihelion, how far from the Sun is it at aphelion?

continued on next page

3. What are comet showers? How are they caused? What is the evidence that a comet shower has actually taken place?

4. What causes comets to fall out of the Oort cloud and enter the inner solar system?

5. In what part of the solar system are comets in the Oort cloud thought to have formed originally?

Questions for "SOHO Reveals the Secrets of the Sun" by Kenneth R. Lang
(PAGES 48-53)

1. Why is it necessary to use a spacecraft like SOHO to observe the Sun? What can it do that cannot be done with observatories on the ground? And why was it necessary to put SOHO into orbit around the Sun, rather than around the Earth (which would have been an easier task)?

2. By using SOHO to measure the motions of the solar surface, astronomers can learn about temperatures beneath the surface. Explain how this is done.

3. Describe the large-scale flow of material in the outer layers of the Sun. In what ways does this resemble the large-scale motions of the Earth's atmosphere?

4. How long does it take material emitted from the Sun in the slow component of the solar wind to reach the Earth? Assume that the speed of the material remains constant, and give your answer in hours.

5. According to the article, astronomers have used SOHO to determine the speeds of hydrogen and oxygen ions in different regions of the corona. Describe how you could do this by examining the spectra of these different regions.

Questions for "Detecting Massive Neutrinos" by Edward Kearns, Takaaki Kajita and Yoji Totsuka
(PAGES 54-61)

1. How many different types of neutrino are there? Which type is produced in nuclear reactions at the Sun's core? Which types were involved in the neutrino oscillation experiment at Super-K?

2. If neutrinos are so penetrating, how can the Super-K experiment detect them at all?

3. Did the Super-K experiment detect neutrinos coming from the Sun? If not, where did the neutrinos in this experiment come from?

4. What is the evidence that one type of neutrino can transform into another?

5. How could neutrino oscillation solve the solar neutrino puzzle described in Section 18-9 of Universe? Does the Super-K experiment prove that this actually is the solution to the puzzle?

Questions for "Mapping the Universe" by Stephen D. Landy
(PAGES 62-69)

1. Landy describes in this article the sophisticated techniques he and his collaborators used to measure the spectra of 26,000 distant galaxies. How does measuring a galaxy's spectrum tell you how far away that galaxy is?

2. What is the horizon size? How is it related to the age of the universe?

3. A density fluctuation, as described in the article, is a region of space in which the density of matter is higher or lower than the average. (a) Explain why lumps in mashed potatoes or oatmeal can be thought of as density fluctuations. (b) How did the scale of density fluctuations in the early universe determine the kind of universe we see today?

4. The power spectrum of the universe (shown in a graph in the article) is much larger on large scales than on small scales. This indicates that the universe is clumpier on those large scales. If the universe were equally clumpy on all scales, what would a graph of its power spectrum look like?

5. The power spectrum of the cosmos has a large peak on scales of around 600 million (6×10^8) light-years. How is this related to the spacing between the giant walls seen in the Las Campanas Redshift Survey?

Questions for "The Evolution of Galaxy Clusters" by J. Patrick Henry, Ulrich G. Briel, and Hans Böhringer
(PAGES 70-75)

1. The gas within clusters of galaxies was not discovered until the Uhuru spacecraft was launched in 1970. Why not? What could Uhuru do that ground-based telescopes could not?

2. (a) In their article, Henry, Briel, and Böhringer give the mass of a typical cluster of galaxies, the fraction of this mass that is in the form of visible galaxies, and the fraction of the remaining mass that is in the form of X-ray-emitting gas. Use this information to calculate (a) the combined mass of the visible galaxies in a typical cluster and (b) the mass of X-ray-emitting gas in a typical cluster. (c) What makes up the rest of the mass of the cluster? (d) Explain why the term "galaxy cluster" is a poor description of what these objects really are.

3. What is the difference between a group of galaxies and a cluster of galaxies? What is the evidence that clusters form from the mergers of groups?

4. A planet, like a cluster of galaxies, loses heat into space by emitting electromagnetic radiation. For a planet, the interior remains at a higher temperature than the surface (see, for example, Figure 8-11 on page 198 of Universe, which shows the temperature at various depths inside the Earth). By contrast, a mature cluster of galaxies is coldest at its very center (see the images labeled "Cluster 1795" in the article). Why is there a difference?

5. How do observations of the evolution of galaxy clusters tell us about the average density of the universe?

Questions for "A New Look At Quasars" by Michael Disney
(PAGES 76-81)

1. In his article, Disney explains that as material falls into a massive black hole, only a certain maximum percentage of its rest-mass energy $E = mc^2$ can be converted into radiation. (a) The luminosity of quasar 3C 273 is about 10^{40} watts, or 2.5×10^{13} times the luminosity of the Sun. At what minimum rate must rest-mass energy fall into the quasar's black hole to provide this luminosity? Recall that 1 watt equals 1 joule per second. (b) What minimum number of kilograms of matter must fall into the black hole each second? (Hint: See Section 18-6 of Universe.) At this rate, how long would it take for an amount of mass equal to the Earth's mass to fall into the black hole?

2. Are all quasars observed to be in host galaxies? What is the interpretation of this result?

3. Explain why the density of quasars in the universe peaked about a few billion years after the Big Bang and has been in decline ever since.

4. Disney suggests in his article that the lifetime of a quasar is no more than 10 million (10^7) years. (a) What fraction is this of the lifetime of a galaxy, as given in the article? (b) To put your answer to (a) in perspective, imagine scaling the lifetime of a galaxy down to a typical human lifetime of 75 years. In this model, for how many weeks would the galaxy contain a quasar?

5. Quasars are thought to appear in galaxies with supermassive black holes. However, a number of galaxies have supermassive black holes but are not quasars. What determines whether a quasar is present in such a galaxy?

Questions for "Gamma-Ray Bursts" by Gerald J. Fishman and Dieter H. Hartmann
(PAGES 82-87)

1. What observations ruled out the mid-1980s idea that gamma-ray bursts originated on nearby neutron stars in our Galaxy?

2. Why was it important to detect spectral lines in the radiation coming from a gamma-ray burst?

3. Describe the model given in the article for how gamma-ray bursters are produced. What are some of the difficulties with this model?

4. Since Fishman and Hartmann wrote their article, a number of additional gamma-ray bursts have been observed that have visible underlying galaxies. Some of these observations indicate that the emission from gamma-ray bursts may be beamed, that is, preferentially aimed in certain directions like the beams of a lighthouse or the beams from a car's headlights. Explain how this beaming effect could explain the extreme brightness of gamma-ray bursts even if the source of the burst is of relatively low energy.

continued on next page

5. In the box "The Gamma-Ray Sky" that accompanies their article, Fishman and Hartmann describe a diffuse glow of photons with energy 1.8 MeV (1 MeV = 10^6 eV) coming from the Milky Way. What are the frequency and wavelength of these photons? How does the wavelength compare to the typical diameter of an atomic nucleus, about 10^{-14} m? (Hint: See Sections 5-2 and 5-5 of Universe.)

Questions for "Surveying Space-time with Supernovae"

by Craig J. Hogan, Robert P. Kirshner, and Nicholas B. Suntzeff
(PAGES 88-93)

1. Do all Type Ia supernovae have the same maximum luminosity? If not, how can they be used as "standard candles" for determining the distances to remote galaxies?

2. A Type Ia supernova reaches its maximum brightness in about three weeks. Why, then, do observations of such supernovae often go on for a year or more?

3. In their article, Hogan, Kirshner and Suntzeff describe the idea that supernovae in distant galaxies might contain fewer heavy elements than those in nearby galaxies. Using what you know about stellar evolution, explain why this might be so.

4. Explain how the surprising dimness of high-redshift supernovae suggests that the universe must have expanded more slowly in the past than expected.

5. Why does the data from Type Ia supernovae indicate that the expansion of the universe is actually speeding up?

Questions for "Cosmological Antigravity" by Lawrence M. Krauss

(PAGES 94-101)

1. Using Hubble's own first estimate of the value of the Hubble constant (given in the article), calculate the age of the universe (a) assuming a zero cosmological constant and a density parameter $\Omega_0 = 0$ (an empty universe), and (b) assuming a zero cosmological constant and a density parameter $\Omega_0 = 1$ (a flat universe). Give your answers in years. (Hint: See Section 28-7 of Universe. Recall that 1 Mpc = 3.09×10^{19} km and 1 year = 3.16×10^7 s.) (c) How do we know that these ages, and thus this value of H_0, cannot be correct?

2. Explain how a cosmological constant could arise from the laws of quantum mechanics. What is the problem with a cosmological constant generated in this way?

3. Describe three different kinds of observations that indicate that the average density of matter in the universe is substantially less than the amount needed for the universe to be flat.

4. Does the nonzero cosmological constant described in Krauss's article have a positive value ($\Lambda > 0$) or a negative value ($\Lambda < 0$)? Explain.

5. The graph in the article entitled "Map of Models" shows that if the density of energy in the cosmological constant were great enough, no Big Bang could have taken place (see the upper left corner of the graph). Explain why.

Questions for "Searching for Life in Other Solar Systems" by Roger Angel and Neville J. Woolf

(PAGES 102-105)

1. Why would the presence of both oxygen and methane in a planet's atmosphere be compelling evidence of the existence of life on that planet?

2. Why is it useful to use a pair of telescope mirrors, rather than a single mirror, to search for planets orbiting other stars?

3. How can dust in our solar system interfere with observations of planets orbiting other stars?

4. Explore the Terrestrial Planet Finder web site (http://tpf.jpl.nasa.gov/) to learn the current status of this mission. When might the telescope be launched? For what other kinds of astronomical research could this telescope be used?

5. In their article, Angel and Woolf suggest a cost of $500 million ($5 \times 10^8$) for the Terrestrial Planet Finder mission. Do you regard this as a reasonable cost for a mission that could provide the first evidence for life beyond the solar system, but that might instead find no evidence for life? What standards of worth did you use in making your decision?